THE BOY AND T

Scenes from Alfred Wallis's St Ives

Albert Rowe

TABB HOUSE
PADSTOW

First Published 2002
Tabb House, 7 Church Street, Padstow
Cornwall, PL28 8BG

ISBN: Please see back cover

British Library Cataloguing-in-Publication Data.
A Catalogue record of this title is available from
the British Library.
Printed by TJ International Ltd, Padstow, Cornwall

CONTENTS

ALFRED WALLIS R.I.P.

IN night-storms listens to
God calling down the chimney.
At first blue morning shine
Casts a bent finger
Into the Bible's black pool
To fish for His meaning.

Morning odd-job man,
He talks aloud to God
As the felloe of his barrow
Burrs out salvation
Over Digey and Fore Street cobbles
To Armour's Olde Curiosity Shoppe:
Though donkey work, God's will be done.

Afternoons, makes pictures
Of ships spellbound in glacier worlds
Pale as Adam-forsaken paradise,
Of great fish under boat keels —
Men's souls return to water —
Of tiny craft placed lovingly in harbour.

"God guides my hand,
Gives me my clouds, quays, boats, fish,
My palette's colours from shells, sea-stones;
Each lighthouse his admonitory finger,
My grand designs, all shapes and angles,
Held equal in the cradle of his eye."

ST IVES BOY'S SUMMER

THE tired high tide
   Turns slowly on her
Back and sleeps. Beside
Me my cat curls, his fur

Warm. I stroke and stroke
It, feel his body slack.
Content to be woke,
From deep in the heaped black

Shine of his body
He begins to offer –
No sound more friendly –
The hugged warmth of his purr.

Sun-ripened granite,
sea-water twin to air;
Gulls immaculate,
Standing drowsily where

The lip of the tide
Rest peaceful on white
Sand, where every stride
Sinks ankle-deep. From its height

The clock, sun-faced, fat,
In its granite tower,
Lets loose gold chimes that
Softly drift each hour

Into the cool shine
Of the calm harbour,
Where dozing in line
The boats rest from labour.

Walk home to dinner?
Another swim? Go climb
Cliffs? My boy's summer,
Sun-blessed, was endless. Time,

A mothering sea,
Was becalmed, green and blue,
Held me lovingly,
As now, me cast up, holds you.

SOLOMON'S FIND

SOLOMON Stevens closed his eyes and lifted his head to let the sun fall full on his face. Blesséd heat, how his body drank it in, until his very bones were warm.

He opened his eyes slightly and squinted through the kaleidoscope of his lids at the sun. The colours he saw were just as magical to him now as they'd ever been.

His mind slipped back over the years to those endless afternoons of summer. There on the sand he stood, a tiny figure by the huge harbour buoy on the Cockbank. He scraped the treacly tar from its iron sides. He *munged* the tar-ball lovingly in his hands, the smell of it like the smell of the harbour full of boats. He tossed it high: the black ball, fired by the sun, flashed heliotrope against the flawless blue.

Tired of his game at last, he climbed to the top of the buoy, round as the world, and lay, sun-soaked, marooned in a sea of blue air. He breathed softly; soft as the sea itself where it slept beyond him in the encircling bay.

But how much faster time ticked now he was old!

Solomon sighed, let his hand fall idly on the warm granite of Doble's Wall where he was sitting. The last lines of Johnny Tucker's song swung into his mind and he sang them aloud:

> "There's no place in all the world
> Like Doble's Wall."

With what emotion the fishermen sang the song of a summer night, Johnny himself accompanying them on his concertina ...

"Solomon!" Solomon stood up hastily and turned to where his wife was standing wide-legged in her doorway.

" 'Es, Loveday, m'dear," he said meekly. He knew she was angry because she'd called him Solomon and not Solly. " 'Es Loveday, my love."

"Lazy laplouse! – How you can sit there 'appy as a bung in

1

a bung-'ole when you d'knaw there edn't two ha'pence in the house to scrape yer backside with, I cean't fathom. And me with 'ardly a mawsel of bread to put inside my lips and my stomach turnin' over like a mack'rel on a spinner."

"Take my life if I wudn't just then thinkin' of 'ow I cud come by a pence or two, Loveday."

"You're a bare-faced liar, you can tell lies aysier than old Jan Launder can swaller sprats, and he clunked down three hunderd for supper that time. I bin standin' 'ere watchin' you, I can read you like a book. You was asleep!"

Solomon cried "I swear to God – "

"Mind He don't strike you down; you'll call upon Him once too often, mark my words! Thinkin' about earnin' a honest pence or two, was you? – I'll take my oath you're even lazier than yer old feyther, and 'e was too lazy to wipe 'is own snout."

" 'Old 'ard, Loveday. Lave my feyther out of it. I wean't 'ear a word against my feyther."

"Then bung yer ears up with bees wax; I'll seh my seh. And yer mother was no more workish than yer feyther, you cud till taties on her floors, the dung was that deep. And the 'igh-water mark around 'er neck was blacker than old Joanna Tregarthen's feet that time they come to lay 'er out, and swore she 'ad on black stockin's as well."

Solomon muttered under his breath "No wonder you're knawn all over St Ives as the Doble Wall Demon." He raised his voice: "The worst day's work in my life was the deh I set foot in Zion Chapel to marry Loveday Nancurvis."

"And that was the only day's work you ever done – and the only night's either, for that matter. You're caught in yer own idleness like a crab in a crabpot. . . . Even if you only went through the motions of findin' a little job, it'd shaw you had some sheame left. . . . Don't aggravate me no more; for the love of the Lord, git out of my sight."

"So I will to once," Solomon replied philosophically.

*   *   *

Solomon began to stroll slowly along the Wharf; he felt like stretching his legs, he'd enjoy a round. Loveday would feel better the minute he was gone, she soon calmed down; she didn't bear him any grudge, he would say that for her.

He passed the Shamrock Lodge. Joe Couch and Ben Penberthy were pacing up and down arguing, as usual, about last Saturday's rugby match. Solomon wondered whether they would come to blows again.

He paused to breathe in the fine clean smoke from their cherry-wood pipes. His mouth watered; he hadn't had a grain of roll tobacco to smoke for well nigh a week.

"Loveday's quite right," he said to himself; "a pence or two wud come in 'andy this very minute for a bit of bread and bacca."

He walked slowly on. Every time he put his left foot down, he felt the warmth of the broad smooth stones through the hole in the tap of his boot.

He turned into the Friendship Cellar, cool and dark and welcoming; he wanted a word with Arthur, the blind basket-maker.

He sat down, watched Arthur weaving a big fish basket, his fingers working as sure as if he had sight: a marvel, that's what it was, a marvel. The rhythmic creak of the withies comforted and lulled Solomon. Their sweet smell reminded him of his boyhood camp among the willows near Clodgy Point.

Arthur, who'd recognised Solomon's footsteps, said at last " 'Ullo, Solly. Ate any lempots lately?"

Limpets, with plenty of vinegar, pepper and salt over them were Solomon's favourite meal – he was almost as fond of them as Jimmy Lempots, so called because he seemed to live off them.

"No, Arthur, not since the deh before yesterdeh. I might, though, go down to Widden Sand directly, or the back of the Old Quay, and pick a frail full for supper." He paused, then asked hesitantly "Eh, you don't happen to knaw a weh I could earn a pence or two, Arthur I s'pose?"

"Loveday, again?"

" 'Es, Loveday again. . . . . Besides, I cud do with a grain of bacca; I 'aven't 'ad a drag on me old pipe for long enough."

Arthur was silent for a while; then, "Why don't you step in to Mikey's shoes and try yer luck?"

Mikey Noonah – that was his nickname, of course – who was one of the St Ives beachcombers, had died the week before. He'd got some of his beer and bacca money by scraping around on the town dump and finding things to sell.

Solomon said "Proper job, Arthur, a 'an'some idea; that's zactly what I'll do – but I 'aven't got a barreh."

"Take Mikey's. It's over there in the corner. He won't 'ave any more use for it now."

"Per'aps," Solomon said solemnly, "they'll give'n a bran' new one up above."

"A golden one, most likely."

"Wi' pearl 'andles, for sure."

The iron felloe of Mikey's old barrow made a pleasant music in Solomon's ears as it rattled over the cobbles.

The town dump lay at the seaward end of Breakwater, a low headland overlooking Porthgwidden Beach. The town council's theory was that the spring tides would carry out to sea all the refuse tipped there. In fact, there was always in existence an area of rubbish about three-quarters of an acre in extent.

The weather was gloriously fine. Every day Solomon went down to the dump; every day he found something worth carting home. It amazed him to see what the gentry threw away: handsome picture frames, bits of carpet, jackets with only a hole or two in the elbows, china just a bit chipped, books and magazines, pieces of brass and lead, iron bedsteads, old boots and shoes – he loaded them all on Mikey's barrow and lugged them home to his cellar to sort. After a bit of work on them, he hawked them all over Downlong and never failed to make a bob or two.

One day he found Mikey's shovel and sieve covered in an old raincoat and hidden under a rock. He remembered that Mikey spent hours on the dump digging up the soft stuff, sand, earth and all, and putting it through the sieve. This must have paid him: Mikey didn't like work any more than he did.

Solomon began to do the same. During that very week he found a sixpence, a two-shilling piece, five farthings, and a gold brooch that turned out not to be gold after all.

It was on a Thursday afternoon three weeks later that he made his real find. There it lay in the bottom of the sieve, plain as Merran Rock in the middle of Widden Sand below.

"My dear life, here's a proper coddle," Solomon said aloud to himself. He bent and picked up the thing from the bottom of the sieve. "Sure as salvation, it's a rale one, otherwise it wudn't shine like that. . . . And I haven't hear tell of nobody that's lost one; I'm certain sure Ab'ram hasn't come round crying it, I wud 'ave 'eard 'im, we all wud with that great bell of 'is, so it's mine all right. . . . 'Ow much shall I git for et, I wonder? One thing I'll warrant: Loveday edn't goin' to knaw about this. She can spend money quicker'n I can ate lempots. No, Loveday edn't goin' to git 'er talons on none of the money I git for this."

The next afternoon Solomon walked down over the Wharf to the Friendship Cellar. He'd no sooner sat down than Arthur said "Well, tell me what's up, Solly; yer mind's jumpin' about like a bunch of herrin' in a net, you're makin' me jump as well."

Arthur listened in silence while Solomon told him about his find.

"And you seh Colenso the jeweller offered you a 'underd and twenty pounds for'n?"

" 'Es."

"And where ez et now?"

Solomon said "I've 'idden et aweh in my cellar. I cean't lave anythin' lyin' about, Loveday poke her nose in everythin'. You d'knaw what a peasy brains I am. I wanted to ask you about et before I done anythin' more."

"Go 'ome to once," said Arthur, "and take it up to Colenso's before he d'change 'is mind."

"Proper job, Arthur, I will to once, sure as the Rock of Ages.

That money will keep me and Loveday for dunkey's years if we go careful. And I shean't have to stir hand, foot nor finger unless I want to. .... Per'aps a bit of diggin' on the dump now and agen of a fine summer's afternoon to keep me in trim and give me a good appetite for a basin of lempots."

"Won't you even give Loveday a little gift?"

"Well for years I've 'ad my eye on that 'andsome calabash pipe up Fore Street in Armour the Old Curiosity Shop winder – it's got a mermaid on the bowl – and that pipe I'm goin' to 'ave, even if the Lord do call me 'ome the minute I lay 'ands on et. .... Aw, Loveday, let me see, now . . . 'es, I'll buy somethin' for Loveday. A nice pair of they thick black wool stockin's, per'aps, fer the wenter; Loveday's always catchin' cold. . . . And a pound of bacca fer you, Arthur, yer favourite plug bacca."

When Solomon got home, he found Loveday standing in the middle of the kitchen. She had on a new fur coat; the kitchen itself was covered with boxes and parcels.

Solomon sank down into his rocking chair by the slab, said " 'Oly Feyther above, Feyther Chrestmas bin 'ere or no, Loveday?"

Loveday danced around the table, rubbing her face against the fur.

"Loveday, love, set down. Tell me what's 'appened, for pity's sake!"

"My ship's come 'ome, I always swore et wud, that's what's 'appened, Solly, my ship's come 'ome. Now, don't utter breath. Let me tell you all about et." She stretched to her full height, sucked in a lungful of air. "Dennertime, after you'd gone out, I went down to the cellar. You knaw what a coddle you lave et in. I thought I'd tidy et up a bit fer you, make et all nice and fitty like. Well, in one corner under a old oilskin, I found a tin."

"Not a bacca tin?"

" 'Es, a bacca tin; et must 'ave bin there for generations. I picked et up to thraw et aweh – and et rattled!"

"No," Solomon groaned faintly.

" 'Es, you, it rattled. I opened et and inside I found – guess what?"

Solomon could only shake his head.

"A pearl necklace, that's what, a rale pearl necklace. 'Ow you cud of missed et, spendin' all yer days in the cellar, I ceant't fathom. That just shaws 'ow slaw you are."

"You 'aven't sold the necklace already, I s'pose?" Solomon's voice quavered in spite of himself.

"Of course I've sold et, peasy brains. No good to me, was et? What do you think I was goin' to do with et? Ate et?"

"Not to Colenso?"

"Colenso? Colenso's meaner than a dogfish, Colenso ez. And a bare-faced robber in the bargain! Colenso? Not likely! I took my pinny off and up Fore Street I went to Long Dick's."

Solomon should his head as if he could not believe his own ears. "A rale pearl necklace I calculate wud be worth nigh on a 'underd and twenty pound," he said, "but I don't su'pose you got anywhere near that much."

Loveday snorted. "A 'underd and twenty? Why, Long Dick give me a 'underd and eighty for et!" She began to prance around the kitchen again. "Like me fur coat, do you? Got et at Martin's. I've always wanted a fur coat. All my life I've wanted a fur coat, swore I'd 'ave one when my ship come 'ome." She paused, bent down over the settle. "And look 'ere, see all the clothes I bought. I've never 'ad a rag to me back all me life 'ardly. Look. 'Alf a dozen pair of they lovely black wool stockin's to keep the cold out in the wenter, Three shifts, I'm tired of they two I made from flour bags, they rasp the skin off yer very back. And look – "

"Loveday, love – " Solomon's interruption was only half-hearted.

" 'Old 'ard, Solly, my cheeld, keep yer tongue between yer teeth a minute longer, I 'aven't forgot 'ee . . . . Close yer eyes and 'old out yer 'and."

When Solomon opened his eyes and looked down, there on his palm was the handsome calabash he'd always wanted.

FOLLOWER

THE donkey and shay halted.
"'Ere you are, slap in front of Aunt Charlotte's door," Nathaniel Tresidder said. "Out you git."

Foolish Georgie and Cock Chit-Chat got down stiffly from the shay and stretched their limbs. It was a fine spring evening; they had enjoyed their ride from St Ives to Lelant, despite their cramped quarters.

Georgie moved forward and spoke to the little grey donkey. "I dearly love you, Jerusalem, I do, my boy. I wish Nathaniel 'ere wud give you to me."

Nathaniel shook his head vigorously. "You can 'ave my old woman with pleasure, but not Jerusalem."

Cock Chit-Chat bent down, looked the donkey full in the face for a bit. "I've just bin picturin' Jerusalem 'ere in your wife's new 'at. The one she wore last Sunday in Zion Chapel. The one with all they cherries and apples and pears and – "

"And a banana," Nathaniel interrupted with relish. "Don't forget the banana."

"'Es, Gospel truth – and a banana. Every time I set eyes on that banana – but never mind that now. 'Er Garden of Eden 'at I named et as soon as I clapped my peepers on et. Brehmee 'andsome she looked en et, too. Well, if Jerusalem 'ere 'ad that 'at on, to 'ide 'er ears, she'd look rale 'uman, in fact the spittin' image of your wife."

"Only prettier." This was the kind of badinage he and Cock Chit-Chat always indulged in, and how they both enjoyed it, especially when the target was his wife.

Nathaniel turned to the squat figure of Georgie, round as a buoy, busy dusting imagined dust from his bark jumper and bellbottomed trousers. "No, Georgie, my son, you can 'ave my old Dutch, and welcome, but you cean't 'ave Jerusalem. Nobody but Death with 'is scythe will ever part Jerusalem and me."

Georgie, a mongol, a relative of my grandmother's, spent

almost all his time in my grandfather's bakehouse, earning his keep – that was the pretence everybody subscribed to – in summer by making the ice-cream; and all year round by doing odd jobs, such as getting the bread tins ready for each batch of bread, and sweeping out the bakehouse, the cockroaches rustling tinnily away.

Cock Chit-Chat was a retired fisherman. He lent Grandfather a hand looking after the pigs, pony and poultry at Breakwater. He, too, spent much of his spare time in the bakehouse, luxuriating in the warmth, and in his unfailing welcome; Grandma was fond of him and spoiled him with pasties, *fooch* and saffron buns.

Another of Cock Chit-Chat's favourite places was the room above our confectioner's shop in front of the bakehouse and overlooking Fore Street. The room was filled for hours with sunlight on a fine summer's day, and contained over fifty bird cages. The birds were mostly canaries, linnets and goldfinches. The canaries Uncle Jacob bred and showed all around the county; the linnets and goldfinches he trapped out Man's Head way.

Here Cock chit-Chat would sit entranced for hours at a time, listening. He could never make up his mind which songs he liked best: in some moods it was the linnets', in others the shining fine silver thread of the goldfinches', and in others again the rich varied songs of the canaries; in particular, the contralto trilling of the rollers . . .

Charlotte, whose house they were now standing in front of, was Georgie's aunt. Whenever Georgie felt like it, he came on a visit; he was so mulishly obstinate that once he made up his mind to do something, there was no dissuading him. Grandda wouldn't trust him to go on his own, so Cock Chit-Chat was ordered to go with him.

Charlotte, smiling her welcome, held the door open, said "Hullo, Georgie, dear, I heard tell you was coming over to visit me, and you've brought Richard with you for a bit of company, I see.

That's grand. Comest on in with you, and have a dish of tay and a mawsel of bread with me."

No sooner had Georgie set foot in the kitchen than he burst out "Pasties, Auntie Charlotte, I can smill pasties. Rich! I d'love to ate one of your pasties, full of tatie and beef and liver and onions and turnip. . . . Rich!"

"What a bustguts you are, Georgie, you 'aven't 'ardly set foot in the house yet," Cock Chit-Chat said. "Fadge, fadge, fadge, nothin' but fadge from the time you open yer eyes till you close them again at night."

Georgie glowered at him, growled "There edn' nobody can make a pasty like she can. I'd rather ate one of Auntie Charlotte's pasties than — "

Charlotte interrupted him; she did not want to hear him compare hers with those he was regularly fed in the bakehouse.

She turned to Cock Chit-Chat, looked at him archly (he was still a fine-looking man and her husband had passed away long ago). "Did you say you didn't want a mouthful of one of my pasties, Richard?"

Cock Chit-Chat, said hastily "No, Charlotte, I certainly dedn't. You're 'avin' a maygame with me, I knaw. Of course I do want a crumb or two of pasty; you knaw full well I like them as much as Georgie 'ere."

"Good, good! I've fitten one for you and I wouldn't like it to be thrown into the pig bin."

Charlotte took Cock Chit-Chat's pasty out of the oven. It was on one of her best flower-decorated dinner plates, and she put it in front of him with due ceremony. It was about average size, a foot-and-a-half long.

She winked at him as she took Georgie's out. It was on a small platter and half as big again as Cock Chit-Chat's.

She said "I've never seen Georgie beaten by a pasty yet, Richard, but this one will beat him, I warrant."

"If Georgie 'ere can clunk this one down, I'll back 'im as pasty-king against anybody in all Cornwall," said Cock Chit-Chat.

The warm savoury smell filled the kitchen. A trickle of brown gravy ran from the corner of Georgie's pasty and formed a little pool on the blue of the platter.

Without a word Georgie dipped his finger in the gravy, sucked it noisily, then fell upon the pasty like a man famished. Cock Chit-Chat was only a shade less quick.

Charlotte sat by the slab grate, near enough to feel the fire, and watched them, a look of pleasurable anticipation on her unlined face.

Cock Chit-Chat finished first and sat back, grunting in utter contentment. Georgie was already more than halfway through his. He was eating doggedly, relentlessly, oblivious of his surroundings, his slanted almond eyes fixed on the pasty.

Charlotte said incredulously "He's going to clear it. Sure as crabs can crawl, he's going to clear it!"

Cock Chit-Chat could only nod, and wait in admiring silence for Georgie to finish, wiping crumbs and the remaining gravy from the platter with his forefinger.

It was already getting dark when the two men said goodbye to Charlotte and set out for home.

"Which weh shall we go, Georgie, my son, back over the 'igh road through Carbis Bay, or down 'Lant Lane and across the Towans?"

"Shortest weh 'ome, Rechard, my 'andsome, shortest weh 'ome."

"Then across the Towans et ez. Shortest weh will suit me; I've got a bunion that's givin' me gyp."

The darkness deepened as they left the main road and plodded down Lelant Lane. The lane was much narrower, the hedges high and hemmed in by dense bushes. The night smell of dank and rotting vegetation filled their nostrils. The very darkness itself was thicker here, clung to them, slowing down their progress. Georgie shivered, thrust his soft childlike hand into Cock Chit-Chat's.

At that precise moment, a long-drawn tremulous call floated towards them from somewhere ahead.

"Wha's that, Rechard?" Georgie gasped, clutching his companion's shoulder.

"You'll have me nervous as a kitten, too," Cock Chit-Chat grumbled, barely disguising the fact he, too, had jumped just as much as Georgie. "Et's only a owl. What ded you fancy et was — a ghost?"

The owl, silent and insubstantial as mist, sketched its wavering curves of white against the blackness. Georgie buried his face in Cock Chit-Chat's jersey as the hunter, oblivious of their presence, swept by close overhead.

"I don' like no owls," Georgie muttered. "They owls bring bad luck, they owls look like death."

"Bad luck or good luck, death or no death, we shean't git 'ome tonight unless we up anchor and up sail and off. Come on, Georgie, my cheeld, hold fast to my 'and."

They walked on in silence. Cock Chit-Chat could feel Georgie trembling by his side, and this did nothing for his own confidence. Georgie began pressing so close that they often stumbled against one another.

When nearing the end of Lelant Lane, Georgie said "I wish we 'adn't come this short weh, Rechard . . . I wish we 'ad gone 'ome the long weh, then we wudn't 'ave to go through 'Lant Graveyard 'ere to git out on the Towans."

"Never mind 'Lant Graveyard, Georgie. There edn' anythin' in the graveyard to 'arm you." Cock Chit-Chat was patently reassuring himself as well as his companion. "There's only the dead — "

"That's what I'm afraid of, all them dead bodies 'ere and — "

Hastily Cock Chit-Chat interrupted him. "Don't be so fulish. The dead aren't goin' to rise up and 'arm you. The dead don't do no walkin' 'ere."

Cock Chit-Chat spoke very loudly, by no means as certain in his own mind that what he said was indeed the truth. 'Ned Lander that time swore 'e 'ad been chased by a ghost,' he thought.

Still gripping Georgie's hand tightly, Cock Chit-Chat led the way over the stile and into the graveyard. They huddled even closer together and struck out uncertainly along the narrow and weed-overgrown path. To left and right the tombstones, menacing as hooded men, rose up from the long grass.

Georgie quavered "Dark, edn't et, Rechard, I cean't see nothin'."

"Blacker than Egypt's night, blacker than man's sinful soul, as Armstone the preacher used to say up Zion Chapel, Lord rest his bones. You — "

Georgie clutched Cock Chit-Chat's arm, stopped dead in his tracks, began to tremble more than ever.

"I . . . I can 'ear somethin' comin', Rechard. 'Ark!"

They stood immobile, half crouching, Cock Chit-Chat as ready to take to his heels as Georgie.

At last Cock Chit-Chat said, sighing with relief as he straightened, "I cean't 'ear nothin'. It's just yer fancy, Georgie, my son."

"No, et edn't." Georgie now had his short soft arms around his companion's waist. "I can 'ear somethin'. 'Ark! Soft foots. . . . And breathin' . . ."

"I cean't 'ear nothin', I tell you," Cock Chit-Chat said forcefully. "Come on, 'ere's the gate. Out on the Towans we go. More room to breathe out there. Not so dark, either. Come on, give 'er reach. Pity there edn't no moon."

They went through the gate, leaving it ajar in their haste. The springy close-bitten turf of the Towans beneath their hurrying feet gave them fresh courage, and soon they slowed down.

Cock Chit-Chat had by now breath enough to speak. "I must confess, Georgie, my dear, I'm just as plazed to be shot of that graveyard as you. I — "

"'Ark, Rechard, 'ark! Somebody walkin' be'ind. . . . Soft foots and breathin' 'ard!"

Cock Chit-Chat bent sideways in his effort to listen: then, "Gospel truth, you're right. There *ez* somebody be'ind us!"

"Beginnin' to snort now." Georgie was clinging to Cock Chit-Chat's waist as if he were drowning.

"Lave me go," Cock chit-Chat cried. "Come on, Georgie, 'e's almost on us, I can feel 'is very breath."

Clumsily they began to run.

"Give'm motor, my boy, I can still 'ear 'im. Give'm motor!"

He dragged Georgie after him, but before they had gone many yards, Georgie collapsed in a moaning heap on the turf.

"I cean't run no further. That gee pasty ez risin' in my gullet and – "

"Me, neither. Stay where you're to. I've got me knuckle-dusters in me pocket. I'll face'n, whoever 'ee ez, even if it's Old Nick 'isself."

The breathing, harsh and thick, was very near now.

Cock Chit-Chat stood over Georgie, slipped his knuckle-dusters on, clenched his fist, shouted "Who are you?"

No answer.

"Who are you, for the second time!"

The silence remained unbroken.

"I'm a great man like a tree, mind. I've got me knuckle-dusters up. If you don't answer for the third time of askin', I'll lambaste 'ome to you right in the face and eyes. . . . Who are you?"

No sooner were the words uttered than a great grey hairy face thrust itself forward, the lips drawn back, the long teeth bare, the breath rattling harshly in its throat.

Cock Chit-Chat struck out wildly, felt the knuckle-dusters crunch against solid bone. An inhuman cry shattered the silence: the hideous face was gone as suddenly as it had appeared . . .

Much later that night two weary figures came down over Tregenna Hill, through the Green Court and into Fore Street. Never had its cobbles felt so welcome beneath their feet. A moment more and they were telling Grandfather their story.

The next afternoon, Grandda summoned Georgie and Cock Chit-Chat to sit in front of him in the bakehouse. In his hand he held a copy of the local paper, *The Times and Western Echo*, which the paper boy had just delivered.

"There's somethin' in 'ere I want to read to you two," Grandda said in his best preacher's voice. "Now 'ark to this."

He put on his glasses, lifted the paper, began to read as if he were delivering a sermon in Chapel:

"Lelant parson and NSPCA determined to *persecute* ruffians if found.

Some time after darkness had fallen yesterday evening, a person or persons unknown committed a brutal and cowardly assault upon the Rev. Solomon Couch's little donkey.

An officer of the NSPCA was speedily on the scene and helped Rev. Couch to render first aid. The little donkey, than which there is no gentler beast, is normally given the freedom of Lelant churchyard. It performs the useful office of keeping down the grass. It has never, so the Rev. Couch is able to aver, been seen to set so much as the tip of a hoof on a grave.

Although the donkey was christened Joseph, the village children, with whom it is a great favourite, call it Follower. The pretty little animal earned this delightful nickname, Follower, because of its habit of following whoever passed through the graveyard."

Grandfather could contain himself no longer. He began to laugh, and so did we. Before he could say another word, Cock Chit-Chat and Foolish Georgie had sneaked out of the bake-house door and were gone.

DOWNLONG CHARACTERS

Man Friday

H E always said he was washed ashore from a vessel carrying coal and timber. He was – so he swore – Cap'n of the craft, the only survivor of the storm. Hanging onto a spar for dear life, that's how he kept himself afloat.

Nobody believed him. We said we did; you could not help but feel truly sorry for him, foodless and shelterless as he was.

I helped him feed my grandfather's pigs, which he kept down at Breakwater. I found Man Friday very good company, although he stank like stale fish. I waited until he lit his stub of a clay, now as brown and grimed as his hands, and had settled himself against the cartwheel in the sun, the door of the carthouse wide open facing the west.

I took good care to keep my distance. "That pipe, so short it's right among your whiskers; they're so bushy, stick out so, it's a wonder they don't catch fire, Cap'n Crusoe." (This was the other nickname I always called him by; I knew how it pleased him.)

My words always brought the expected reply. "See thayse whiskers, m'son? I got thayse whiskers from the skipper of a boat called *Salvation*. A fine big boat she was, too. Et was a awful gale, a ninety-knot gale, or my name edn't Cap'n Crusoe – Painter, et ez, but we'll let that pass. The wind . . . the wind was strong enuff to blaw the print off the page of a noospaper. . . . Well, the skipper – I wuz at the 'elm at the time – the skipper, a gee fellah with a chest like the 'arbour bye on the Cockbank, and a voice that rasped the skin off yer ears, poked 'is gee bran-tub of a 'ead from belaw and – can 'ee guess what 'appened?"

Hastily I said "No, I cean't, Cap'n Crusoe," though I could have told you the story word for word. "No, I cean't, Cap'n Crusoe."

"Well, the very next second, that gale blawed aweh 'is whiskers, all in one go, right onto my chacks, and 'ere they've stuck ever since!"

He'd collapse then in a fit of dry retching laughter, followed by a spasm of coughing that shook his shrivelled humped body and sent the droplets of spittle flying from his cracked lips until his grey bush of a beard was beaded, bright in the evening sun.

Dipping into the inside pocket of the overcoat he wore beneath another one, he wiped away the shining drops. The paper folded carefully, he tucked it away in the pocket of the overcoat he wore outside.

He'd finish his pipe and put the stubby clay away, patting the still-warm bowl to make sure it was safely lodged, before he began to stir the pig swill steaming and bubbling in the big boiler, pig swill I had fetched from Hotels Chy-an-Albany, Chy-an-Drea and Chy-an-Olva in our pony and trap.

Stirring, sniffing the heaving mixture, he'd choose his own big basinful. By the time he had fed the pigs, by now squalling fit to beat the band, the swill would be cool enough for him to clunk down, glancing about him as if he was afraid somebody was going to take the bowl from him.

Once he found a whole duck in the swill. Held it aloft. Shouted to me "Look, my cheeld, a whole duck!" He sniffed it noisily. "Bit 'igh, that's all, but not so 'igh as they pheasants and all that muck the gentry do ate. A whole duck! Chrestmas and me birthdeh, all in one." He began to devour it, but paused long enough to cry "Rich, me cheeld, rich! A rale love feast, sure 'nuff, a rale love feast!"

And how the nerves of the housewives who lived close to Breakwater in Carncrows, Teetotal and St Eia Street were stretched to breaking point twice a day by the screeching and squalling of the pigs. Why did the town council allow it, that's what they wanted to know.

And just as bad, the Breakwater roosters who started their din, fit to waken the dead, before first light.

*   *   *

Foolish Georgie, Bakehouse Boy

LOCKS himself in the bakehouse loo until others, desperate, begin to beat the door down.

Comes out at last, oblivious, and brushes imaginary dust from his bellbottoms and bark jumper. Takes off his cap and dusts his tiny boots, already scrupulously cleaned that morning.

Goes into the linney, grunts as he turns the handle of the ice-cream machine, the ice packed around the container crunching.

Grumbles, mutters forbidden words to himself as he pushes the barrow with the container in its ice-jacket to Ward's ice-cream cart on the Wharf.

He is sweating when he comes back and mops his face with a red handkerchief before sitting down in the linney. We children gather round, wait for him to pitch the note and sing falsetto:

> "There's a friend for little children
> Above the bright blue sky,
> A friend who never ages,
> A friend eternally."

we children joining heartfelt in.

We watch his soft child's hands tapping out the time, his blanched hairless forty-year-old ageless face entranced, his slanted oval eyes fixed fast on Jesus, eternal Child, loving Father he never had.

Hymn finished, he leads us without pause in our favourite Sunday-school verse: " 'Suffer the little children to come unto Me, for of such is the Kingdom of Heaven'," our warm tears falling like manna to the cold floor.

Janie Hard Charles, Dogfish Skinner

EVERY morning she comes, hair cut like a man, woodbine perpetually stuck to her lower lip. She sets up her trestle table, the five hooks above her within comfortable reach of her raised arms, and stirs the pile of dogfish lying at her feet on the sand. She knows the fishermen in front of the Shamrock Lodge above are looking at her, and making their usual criticisms. Well, let them; she'll show them who's the best skinner still between here and Johnie Groats.

Only the stir of her great tits as she stoops, picks up a dogfish from the heap, rams its head on the savage hook above her, in one defiant gesture tears skin from body, slams the body on the trestle table, slits it from gills to tail, tears out the guts, the stinking yellow eggs trembling, cuts off the head and tail, with the long blade of her knife sweeps the offal to the sand, throws the body into the waiting barrel, betrays her sex.

She sucks the blood from one slimy finger, spits the blood out onto the sand. Dogfish spurs, worse than the devil. No wonder the fishermen's hands are cut to pieces trying to untangle them from the nets. The nets, too, damaged but serve the sods right, they and their tongues.

As to eating dogfish, we would rather starve than eat them. Call them some fancy name – rock salmon, wasn't it? – and send them up country for the foreigners to eat; good riddance to bad rubbish; they foreigners will eat anything.

Voice harsher than her oilskin apron, Janie stands wide-legged in her stink, looks up and curses every mother's son of them.

Cock Chit-chat

COCK Chit-Chat stands in the carthouse door in the sun.

"Fetch me a pail of wehter, m'boy, and me soap and towel. I had a wash this mornin', but only a lick and a promise. . . . Ah, that's right. Proper job. Put the pail right there in the eye of the sun. A good scrub over now, I feel dirty. . . . You d'knaw what I do think, I've told 'ee often enuff: Cleanliness is next to Godliness."

"That's why," I said, keeping a straight face, "they call you

Dick Cleanliness behind your back, instead of your other nickname, Cock Chit-Chat." (His real name is Richard Stevens.) "Keep yer tongue between yer teeth and 'ark to me. Et don't matter what they call me, as long as my Lord and Saviour don't fergit to call me on the appointed deh to set in glory with all the chosen saints up above. The very thought of being cast into outer darkness, like some I knaw, is enuff to frighten me to death. – And now to 'ave that scrub!"

I love to see this fine man stripped to the waist, to watch his great muscles jump and twitch as he washes off the suds and dries his huge shoulders and chest on the flour sack he keeps so scrupulously clean. And as I look, I promise myself that I will someday be as fine a man, with shoulders and muscles as big.

I watch in silence as Dick pulls on his jersey and smooths down his hair, still as abundant as when he was a lad.

"No sun on me body for me. Sun do take every bit of nature out of any man's skin, lave it dry and scaly as the back of a dogfish that's bin lyin' too long in the sun. . . . But me face, me face ez diff'rent. Me face has stood up to the sun and the wind and the say so long, et's like a piece of boot leather. Me face, me face don't matter; who's goin' to look at me face?"

He sits down, the sun full on his face, fills his cherrywood pipe, clears his throat and begins to sing in his rich bass his best-loved hymn, 'Rock of Ages cleft for me,' I joining in the second verse, his favourite and mine, with an improvised descant.

How we boys could sing in our school, the Board School in the Stennack! Our headmaster, C.H. Bray, took us for singing, so we had to sing our hearts out, as Dick and I were singing now:

> "Nothing in my hand I bring,
> Simply to thy Cross I cling:
> Naked come to Thee for dress;
> Helpless, look to Thee for grace;
> Black, I to the fountain fly,
> Wash me, Saviour, or I die."

The last verse finished, we look at each other and smile. Dick pats my bristly hazel-nut head – always bristly because instead of going to Sam Kemp, the barber, for a haircut, I always went up the Stennack to Couch's stables and asked to have the horse clippers put over my head. It didn't take a minute. Afterwards I spent the twopence my mother gave me on *nicey*.

Long since a widower, Dick's only son had been lost at sea; and long since, too, I had lost my own father.

Dick rises and stretches, his chest pushed out round as a barrel. Without a word, we smile at each other again. I know what he wants. He hands me the money and I hurry along Island Road to Straddles – that was the baker's nickname – to buy him a freshly-baked saffron cake for his tea.

Dicky

UP and down, up and down on the Wharf he touts, the top of his yachtsman's cap whiter than visitors' faces.

"Seal Island, ladies, gents, a trip to Seal Island? Boat now leavin' the pier."

He steps forward, nods as freely as if he knew them. His thin tobacco-stained lips smile, but his eyes are cold, embittered with envy of this foreign trash.

Better this, though, than being sodding carpark man, catching cheats, but caught himself fiddling a bob or two. Getting the boot. Being told he ought to be ashamed of himself, as if it was only he who was at it. What about the others? You ought to see what all them councillors and officials get up to.

Better also than being deck-chair man on Mester Sand. Lugging all them deck-chairs to and fro – heavy and awkward as hell them deck-chairs – working long hours for a few bob.

Summer season over, the awakened winter winds in sole possession now of the beach, Dicky once more becomes the solitary beachcomber, a role as familiar as his old jacket.

Wait for high tide, the rollers curling in, all bright white hissing foam, a handsome sight. Best of all, when it was ground sea, the criss-cross waves turning over the clean Mester Sand, you never know what you'll find . . .

Suddenly he darts forward, ragged trousers drenched, stoops, grabs something, holds it aloft in triumph . . .

Once he found a thick wedding ring, solid gold. Sold it to Andrew Armour. Got a good price. Drank the winter away, caring for nobody . . .

Beachcombing over, daylight drained away, bread and treacle for supper unless he's lucky and been given some fish, he rejoins his life again in the Sloop Inn. There, ferrets around for an artist to sponge from; anybody will do, though you can't be sure of them these days, not like the old days when artists were artists. Old John Park, with his red light of a nose and his trembly hands — how could he paint them lovely pictures with trembly hands like that? He was soft, was old John, you could rely on cadging a pint from him. Harry Rowntree, too, you only had to say you liked his caricatures on the walls in the bar, for him to dip his hand into his pocket.

No good now tapping they artists in the Round Bar, you'd think they'd bought it — too neary to give you the skin off their turd, they were.

No artists in the Sloop tonight, Dicky looks for a stranger to tell the tale to. Anything about boats and the sea: they'll believe anything, them strangers will. Fools and their money are soon parted. They like to treat you, it makes them feel important. Proper bigshits they are, too big for their own boots. But that's all right, as long as they stand you a few pints. You can drink all night, your pack of lies don't do no harm; they love it.

If he's not in luck, Dicky reluctantly spends his own hard-earned cash.

He sits till chucking-out time. By then he's swilled enough. He sways through the doors and staggers along Back Lane to his cold, cold empty house, not a crumb left to eat.

He gropes aimlessly around, at last falls on his bed and down into darkness where bitter tongues spitting out their contempt of him are silent.

He wakes shaking next morning, goes out to slip between men's fingers like some starved homeless cat that offers no angles to sharp winds and sharper corners – seeking something, always seeking, seeking, but never finding.

THE BOY AND THE PAINTER

IT was soon after his wife's death that I became friends with Alfred, and all because I admired one of his paintings.

I remember the incident vividly. I was coming back from Porthmeor from a swim — I must have been eight or nine at the time — and as I drew level with Alfred's front door, which was open, I stopped and looked at the painting.

It was of a schooner sailing on a green and white sea. On the horizon was a lighthouse, and in the foreground was part of a familiar-looking headland. Obviously, it was our own St Ives bay that Alfred had painted. The lighthouse was Godrevy Lighthouse and the headland was part of Porthminster Point.

But what fascinated me was the big fish that swam directly below the schooner. Although it was supposed to be swimming in the sea *beneath* the schooner, it was painted as plainly as if it were laid out flat on the surface for all to see. It was a beauty, with a blunt head and a fine curling tail. And it was huge — bigger than the schooner itself, in fact.

I liked the painting very much. Although I thought I could paint better boats than that, the fish was splendid, far better than anything I could do.

When Alfred came and stood in his doorway, I told him how much I liked the painting.

" 'Aw, you do, do 'ee?" he said in his deep, gruff voice, surprisingly loud for such a small man. "She was a fine boat, was the *Tribulation*. I was cap'n of 'er, you knaw."

I nodded, said she looked a fine craft, sure enough.

"An' the fish," Alfred said, "I s'pose you're like all the other tomfools that pass up an' down, you do think the fish ruin the picture?"

"No," I said emphatically, "I d'think it's one of the handsomest fish I ever saw."

"An' you don' think et's too big?"

"No, I don't!"

"An' you don' think et shuldn't be there, like all the other blessed fools keep tellin' me?"

This was too much for me and I burst out "Well, they *are* fools, sure 'nuff, if they seh that. Why, it's the best part of the picture. That fish, it's . . . it's a rale beauty."

A smile warmed Alfred's dough-coloured face and he whispered hoarsely "Ah, you're like me, boy, you're wise." He grinned secretively and patted me on my close-cropped head. Then, without warning, he shouted "Dam' fools, all ob'm!"

I stepped back in alarm, but he smiled as suddenly as he'd shouted. Brushing back his grey Crippen moustache, he added "I'll tell 'ee somethin' now. See that fish? That fish d'stand for all the fish that ever swum – for all the fish God ever put in the say. Tha's why it's so big an' powerful."

"I see that all right," I said, nodding my hazel-nut head.

"Come yer ways in," he said, "I've got a better picture to shaw 'ee."

I followed Alfred in. He stopped at the kitchen table, took off several stained layers of newspaper that served as a tablecloth.

The whole of the round table top was covered by a painting. It was another of St Ives Bay, with Godrevy Lighthouse in the background. But this time a large fleet of mackerel boats scudded across a seal-grey sea. Under each boat's keel was a fish, shaped like a dolphin, yet magically different, each as long as the boat itself.

"Lovely fish," I said sincerely. I didn't think much of the boats, for they were of a kind I'd drawn when I was much younger, and I could do better now. But the fish were wonderful, so full of life I wouldn't have been surprised if they'd swum right off the table.

"I'll tell 'ee somethin' about them fish," Alfred said. He lowered his voice, glanced towards the stairs that led up to the bedroom. "I don' want *she* to 'ear. She's up there, you knaw. They all do think she's dead, but she ednt." He scuffled across to the bottom of the stairs, his loose grey jersey flapping about his tiny body, and cried "I d'knaw you're listenin', you black-'earted woman!"

He came back to the table looking very pleased with himself. "She do like to 'ark," he chuckled, "but she don' like nobody to knaw she's 'arken." He paused and his face took on the look I'd seen on the faces of Old Testament prophets in my Bible picture books, an out-of-this-world look. "Now about them fish. Each boat in that fleet – there was over one 'undred an' twenty ob'm when I was a young man, and now there is only a few ob'm left, an' even they 'ave got motors aboard – no mackerel boat shud 'ave a motor! – each boat of that fleet had a soul, a 'an'some soul shaped like a fish. So they fish I painted edn't fish at all . . . You wudn't be no good without a soul, wud 'ee, boy?"

"No," I said hastily, "nobody wud."

"They boats wudn't, neither, see? Tha's why I've painted 'em complete, souls an' all, see, boy?"

I said again utterly sincere, "Of course, I see."

"Now I've got another 'an'some picture up in the bedroom. You'd like to see that one, wudn't 'ee?"

I hesitated.

Alfred laughed. "I d'knaw what's the matter wi' you. You're afraid of *she*. But you needn't be. Et's all right. I've got 'er locked in the cupboard. She's always got 'er 'ear to the door to 'arken', but she cean't get out till I let 'er. Once a day, an' that's enuff for she . . . Come on up, boy."

As I followed Alfred up the narrow stairs, I comforted myself that there would be nothing up there, it was all in Alfred's daft old head. Yet I still went up very slowly, glancing behind me: how glad I was to see the front door was still open.

Alfred was waiting for me on the landing. He held open the bedroom door. "There," he said softly, "look there, boy. On the front of the cupboard. She's *inside*, an' 'er likeness is *outside*."

I stared, fascinated, more than a little frightened. The whole of the front of the cupboard, a cupboard big almost as a wardrobe, was covered by a life-size painting of a woman. She was dressed in black from head to foot: black buttoned-up boots, black floor-length heavy skirt, tight black blouse fastened at the throat with a big yellow brooch, black beads wound tightly around her throat. Her face was grey, long and rectangular, her nose hooked, her eyes big and staring, with bulging black eyeballs. Her hair, black and glistening, was piled high in a triple bun on top of her head.

I could not take my eyes off her. Although the figure was crudely done, it had an eerie, almost hallucinatory, force and life about it . . . And the eyes, the eyes, I became convinced, the eyes were beginning to look full at me.

I half turned.

Alfred said sharply "No, don' go. Come on in. Et's only a paintin'. She cean't get out, the black-'earted woman. . . . See the 'alter round 'er neck?"

I stepped cautiously into the box-like bedroom and nodded: my throat was so dry I could not utter a sound.

"Well, that 'alter is fastened to the gibbet, see, in the corner of the picture." He cackled sharply, "An' I'm the 'angman, only I 'aven't put myself in the picture. An' see that brooch she got on?"

I could only nod again.

"That's the one I give 'er. I got'n from Armour up the Old Curiosity Shop. Gold. Like to see it, wud 'ee?"

I shook my head violently.

Alfred ignored me. "She wanted to be buried in'n, but I took 'n off 'er before they screwed 'er down, black-'earted bitch."

I'd had enough. I managed to say "I must go now, Alfred, or I'll be late for denner." Stumbling out of the bedroom, I scrambled down to the kitchen.

Alfred followed me down, stood wide-legged close to me. "Wait till you're like me," he said bitterly, wiping the drop that dangled from the end of his nose between his finger and thumb. "Wait till you've seen more denner-times than denners!"

When I repeated this remark at home, my grandfather, Alfred's stepson, resolved to provide him with a hot dinner each day. I had to be the one to take it to him; because of an old family quarrel, no one else in the family would be allowed to set foot inside Alfred's front door.

My reception was always the same. Alfred would ask "What 'ave you got between them there two plates?"

I'd answer "Yer denner, Uncle Alfred."

Alfred would reply "Cold as 'er feet up above, I warrant." He'd lift the plates, replace them. "Call that muck denner? Take'n back to yer cussed gran'fer.

Before I could even pretend to take the plates from the table, he would mutter "Jus' this once. Tell yer cussed gran'fer not to send any more, or I'll thrown'n under the grate." He would then hand me the two plates from the day before, always unwashed.

Often I'd catch him painting a picture. He used the sort of paint and brushes you paint your house with. Very queer, I thought. He painted on anything he could lay hands on: bits of cardboard, which he cut into all kinds of shapes, and bits of plywood he got from Armour's shop, where he did odd jobs now and again.

Sometimes I'd openly admire a picture; sometimes, depending on his mood, he would give it to me. During the time I carried dinners to him, he gave me upwards of a dozen.

Everyone at home laughed at them, assured me a child of five could paint better. Mother said they'd come in handy to light the fire with. I wouldn't hear of it, stored them away in the cupboard in my attic bedroom. The more I looked in secret at the pictures, the more I liked them, especially the colours of the sea. They were *my* pictures. Besides, I couldn't bear to think of all those lovely fish being burned.

One day Alfred received me differently. He sat slumped over the round table in the kitchen. I remember noticing how far his ears stuck out from his closely-cropped head, how big his hands were, how slender his wrists. His face as he glared at me was more dough-coloured than ever.

"Yer gran'fer is tryin' to p'ison me," he burst out in his hollow voice. "I've 'ad pains 'ere in me bowels all this blesséd night . . . Take the muck back. I don' want 'is denner. I wean't never ate another mawsel of 'is."

More than a little upset, I said soothingly "I've just aten one like it, Uncle Alfred, and I'm all right, look. You've just caught a cold or somethin', that's all."

Hastily, I put the plates on the table and hurried out. No sooner had I cleared the door than I heard the crash of breaking crockery.

Alfred followed the same course the next day and the next. The fourth day he looked much better, but behaved even worse.

"You're all in the same boat," he shouted as soon as I went in. "In the same boat you all are, all tryin' to p'ison me. Yer gran'fer started et, and now yer mawther is at et. I knaw what she do want. She d'want my wife's brooch, all gold et is, but she wean't get 'n. I've 'iden 'n away, see? An' you, boy, you're in'n too. You're jilous of me painting – I d'naw you' d'paint – but I can paint better than you, so you don' want me to paint no more."

Deeply hurt, I backed away.

"An' I d'knaw who put you all up to et," Alfred thundered. He sprang across to the foot of the stairs, yelled "Et's you, you black-'earted bitch who put them all up to et!"

He turned, rushed back to the table. Had I not been quick, I should have been struck by the plates as he threw them through the door after me.

Thoroughly frightened and upset, I ran home. Anger now ousting my other feelings, I dashed up to the attic, took the bundle of pictures out of the cupboard, scurried down to the cellar, there broke them up and fed the fire with them.

THE SEINE FISHERMEN

"HEVVA! Hevva!"

From the huer's hut at the top of the cliff above Porthminster Beach, the lookout shields his eyes with his hand. Yes, no doubt at all, there's a school of pilchards coming in – a big one – the inshore sea has turned dark with them.

"Hevva, hevva! Hevva, hevva!"

His warning shouts, louder this time, startle the gulls dozing on the beach below, speeds past Pednolver Hotel and on across the clinkered sides of the Arts Club. Over the barnacled, limpeted hump of Crab Rock, favourite spot of Borlase Smart, Stanley Spencer and other artists, the harsh shouts alert the helpers on West Pier, Wharf Road, the Wharf itself.

They smile at each other, nod, hurry along Pednolva Walk and through the narrow Warren, their thoughts full of fish, until they reach Porthminster Beach.

The crew in the elliptical, forty-foot-long seine boat lying afloat off shore rouse from under the shady canopy. All action now, they unship the heavy oars, begin to row, their eyes on the lookout. Bush covered in white calico in each hand, the huer signals, guides them to where the sea glows dark, reddish-brown. By now the school of pilchards is gathered; bigger even than he had first thought.

The master seiner in his little boat gives the order. The crew in the seine boat itself begin to pay out the quarter mile of seine net, seventy-foot deep. The two strong men in the master seiner's boat are at full stretch guiding the net.

Slowly, slowly, the great seine encircles the fish, now thrashing so close together you could not put a finger between their quivering, scaly bodies, a foaming blaze in the sun.

The capstans ashore are already fully manned. Amid a deafening welter of cries, the yelling, shouting, laughing helpers are thrusting all their weight against the capstans' long poles.

Slowly, slowly, inch by hard-won inch, the huge meshed

purse closes miserly around the leaping bewildered fish, is winched shoreward, their scales sparkling.

The men in the tow-boat on the seaward side of the seine begin to beat their oars on the surface of the sea to prevent the frantic surging fish from leaping upward and outward and away to liberty in the limitless sea.

In the shallows the clamouring gulls, thick as snowflakes and as white, dive, triumphantly rise, blood-tipped beak clamped around the writhing body of a pilchard. They are ignored: plenty, plenty of fish for all.

The crew in the tow-boat, alongside the seine boat now, dip up the fish in their tuck net, empty them into the punts, which ferry them ashore.

There the carters and their assistants are ready, scoop the fish into baskets, the slippery bodies now becoming still in the cruel air. The baskets are transferred to the waiting carts, the horses standing belly-deep in the sea. Snorting, heaving, the horses are urged forward, strong hands and shoulders keeping the wheels turning as they sink in the soft sand.

The carts, piled high with August pilchards, make their noisy way to the Porthmeor fish cellars, shadowed by boys who snatch up falling fish. The bolder among them seize their chance to *kaybe* fish from the high-piled baskets, avoiding with ease the too-slow whips.

In the narrow Downlong streets, hooves and iron-rimmed wheels striking fire from the cobbles, uncountable cats skulk wide-eyed, hungry, alert, claws unsheathed to grab fish as they slide down. Cats of all ages, shapes, sizes, colours, quarrel over the booty. One notorious tom, a tiger-striped tabby, leaps onto a cart, seizes a pilchard, growls defiance, springs down, stalks away, head held high to keep the fresh fish clean.

The unlucky cats on silent feet follow the yearned-for feast to the cellars, there to join their fellows, the cellar cats, that in the pilchard season ignore the rats, their sustenance in fishless times.

In the cool-shadowed cellars, the carters tip the scaly sheen of fish in slithery heaps. There the watchful women lay them in long rows against the back wall side by side, heads pointing forward, salting each layer down before beginning the next.

The toilsome work goes on and on and on, weary children with small baskets bringing them fish scooped from the central heaps.

The to-and-froing carts, the horses breathing harshly, strength almost spent, stop coming at last.

The ebbing daylight drifts away. The salted fish glow mysterious flickering mother-of-pearl as the layers rise as high as the women can reach.

The candles are lit. In their smoky, uncertain flames, cats, more shadow that substance, flit in and out, snatch a fish from the edge of a pile, melt away, settle happily in some known hide-out, there to savour at leisure the sweet stolen fish.

Work finished at long last, the exhausted women lift their tired eyes, give thanks to God for the harvest He has blessed them with, and pray to Him that it will never . . . never . . . never fail.

THE TOWN CUP

A S the punt took us from Pednolva Point to the Committee Boat, I saw that the boy who had gone away to some private school or other – he lived Uplong, so I didn't know him – was wearing what looked like a woman's woolly dressing gown, which reached almost to his ankles.

I exchanged glances with the other competitors, all from Downlong. What, I asked myself, has he got that thing on for? He can't be cold. The sun's hot and there isn't much of a wind – not nearly enough for my liking; I'm used to swimming in choppy seas.

I had changed into my bathing drawers, made of two big handkerchiefs with tapes to tie it on, on the rocks in front of the bathing shed. The rocks were black with spectators, as was the beach itself, for the annual 'Regatta and Swimming Matches' was one of the two events everybody looked forward to, the other being the Carnival.

The spectators, including the women and girls, I ignored. As Ma said, I'd not got anything they hadn't seen before, and the shed stank too much of piddle for me to change in there.

We climbed aboard the *Ebenezer*, all dolled out with flags, it was her turn to be Committee Boat this year. The planks of her deck had been so well scrubbed you could eat your dinner off them, and there was only the faintest smell of fish.

I looked at the Mayor in his robes and chain, his wife in a flowered dress and hat, saw that they were sitting on padded chairs with arm rests, and wondered where they had come from – not from the skipper's house, that was certain.

I sat on the rail and looked out over the course. The sea was only a bit choppy. If there'd been a good chop, spray coming off the tops of the wavelets, then the chances were the boy from Uplong would get a mouthful or two and that would slow him down.

*　　*　　*

I scanned the sky: not a sign of a cloud, but perhaps the wind would freshen before the race was over; you couldn't tell with this weather.

I shrugged. What was the good of wishing? Whatever the conditions, I was determined to win the Cup this year. That was what everybody expected, including those who had it in for me, even though they hoped I would get beaten.

I knew I could beat the other boys from Downlong. Apart from anything else, they hadn't trained as hard as I had: the length of Porthminster Beach and back, day in, day out (except Sundays, of course), about twelve hundred yards, so we'd always been told, and the race itself was only six hundred yards, so. . . . But this boy from Uplong, I didn't know anything about him. Despite myself, a shadow of a doubt began to darken my mind.

The best thing to do was to go over again what my young uncle, Tom, had told me. As a previous Cup winner, the youngest ever, I believe, I had to heed his advice. Alderman Craze had given him his cup. Huge it was, but only silver plate. (How could it have been anything else that size, that's what everyone said as they saw it in Josh Behenna's window.) But the cup for my race was small and made of pure silver, with pretty patterns on it. I could almost draw the patterns, I'd stood so long in front of Josh's window looking and longing.

Tom's advice: "Keep to the right of him – you turn to your left to breathe – then you can see him all the time. It's one hundred and fifty yards to the flag, so the race is out and back twice. It's a test of stamina more than speed. You've trained hard, I'll give you that, so you should last the course easily.

"Let him stay ahead going out to the flag. Never more than half a body length, though. That way, you'll keep out of his dead water. Before you reach the flag, open up and cut across his bow. Round the flag first, keeping close. Then kick up a splash in his face. . . . Don't look like that, it's fair. You don't want that fancy boy from Uplong to beat you, do you? If you do, I don't. Not a member of my family, I don't.

"Now, when you kick a few splashes in his face – he swim flat,

I've seen him, some fancy stroke he's been taught – that'll knock some of the stuffing out of him.

"Do the same rounding the Committee Boat flag. . . . And on the second lap, do exactly the same as on the first. . . . Make sure, though, you've got enough wind left to go all out the last fifty yards if you have to. . . . And remember, the race isn't won till you hear the gun."

I nodded: Tom was right: I would follow his advice.

I looked out into the bay to where the skiffs were racing. *Maid Marion* was first around the far mark, as usual, followed by Mr Comley's *Bluebird*. Good.

The thousand yard race for men had just finished. John F. Toman, the local hero and many times champion of Cornwall, had just beaten Leo Tregenza by only a yard or two. The people on the rocks were still clapping him enthusiastically. No wonder: they all knew that Penzance man, Tregenza, trained all the year round in Egypt, where he was a lecturer, while John F. could only train in summer across Porthgwidden Beach; and even then some days it was too rough. Of course, that race was the most important, and I hoped that some day I would follow in John F.'s footsteps and win it. Yet I also knew that the Town Cup race was the one most of the spectators were the keenest to see, and this made me all the more determined to win it.

Mr Bidgood, the starter, warned us to get ready. The boy from Uplong took off his woolly frock thing. I saw how smooth and rounded his limbs were, how long and smooth the muscles of his arms and legs. Much taller than me, too, he was; he certainly looked as if he could swim, fancy stroke or no fancy stroke. The crawl it was called, wasn't it?

For a second, I doubted my own ability, but not for more than a second: the thought of how much my widowed mother had built on this was more than enough to strengthen my resolve.

Mr Bidgood handed us our caps; I'd seen from the programme mine was blue, my favourite colour, and I took this as a good omen.

Fred Thomas had cried off just before we went on board. Said he had a bad cold, was feeling sick. None of us believed him, he always had been a coward.

This left only five starters; there had to be six diving off for the third boy to get his prize. Mr Bidgood announced through his megaphone in his lovely deep bass voice – I always thought he ought to have been a singer like Ernie White –- that Jacob Ward would sportingly fill the gap. This was, of course, my other uncle's moment of glory, though we all knew he would only swim the stipulated fifty yards before giving up with the cramp. A good enough excuse; the water was always cold for the Swimming Matches.

The boy from Uplong stood up, went around shaking the competitors' hands, wishing them luck. . . .

Luck, I thought. Who in their senses would wish boys you're swimming against luck? As well as shaking their hands? Daft - he must be daft. I did not put out my hand when the boy came up to me. Then I noticed that Mr Bidgood was watching and thought I ought to make a gesture; a quick touch would be enough.

We lined up on the plank lashed to the boat's side. I stood so that the boy was on my left. This boy had done his training in a bath, so they said. A bath, for heaven's sake, who'd ever heard of such a thing? In warm water, too. A good thing: when he dived off, our water would come as a shock to him, he would have a job catching his breath for a bit, he would.

Luckily Mr Bidgood used a pistol to start the swimming races. If he'd used that great double-barrelled shotgun he started and finished the skiff races with, we would all have fallen in with fright.

The pistol cracked: we dived.

I sprinted about twenty yards. When I glanced across, I expected to see the boy's yellow cap behind me. There *was* no yellow cap. I lifted my head, peered in front: the boy was three or four yards ahead.

I increased my pace, though I hadn't bargained for this. It was a long time – far too long – before I got to the boy's shoulder.

As I planned, I tried to cut across his bow to reach the flag first. I failed. Fortunately, the boy went too wide rounding it. I swam across his feet, grazed the flag stick with my shoulder, knew that the boy was directly behind me in my dead water, kicked up a splash, felt him drop back a bit.

I slowed down. I was puffed and wanted a breather. I waited until my rival passed me. This time I was ready for his spurt and kept level with his shoulder.

Before we reached the Committee Boat flag at the end of the first lap, the boy suddenly cut in, rounded the flag so closely I had to give way and round it on the outside.

I now found myself in the same position as when we dived off. Striving to catch my opponent, who had a three yard lead.

This forced me to swim faster than I wanted. Even so, I sprinted when some distance from the far flag. This time I succeeded in rounding it first, though I feared it was draining the strength I was going to need.

I lifted my head: how far the finishing flag near the Committee Boat's stern seemed to be! Then to my joy I saw that the chop was much higher, the tops of the wavelets broken into white spray.

I blessed the sudden breeze, struck out for home with renewed strength, confidence high.

A few yards more, though, and the boy drew level with me. I realised then that somehow I was going to have to swim the last two hundred yards faster than I had ever swum them before if I was going to win.

Neck and neck, stroke for stroke, we swam, neck and neck, stroke for stroke.

Halfway home, my lungs felt as if they were on fire. Instinctively I quickened my stroke; this was the only way I could gulp down the air fast enough into my starved lungs.

Suddenly, I found I was ahead: my rival had dropped back. Was it the heavy chop that was doing for him? Or was it he hadn't trained as hard as I had?

I felt my arms beginning to tire, my scissors kick become less wide and snappy. Yet somehow I kept up my sprint, gasping like a man drowning. Was it fear that drove me on? Fear of the disgrace – for that was what it was in my eyes – of being beaten?

Whatever it was, over the last fifty yards I sprinted even faster: I felt my rival was right behind me, was gaining on me.

By now I was not even sure where the finishing flag was, how near I was to it. As the pistol sounded, I looked across to see who it was the gun had gone off for.

Relief flooded over me. Yes, it was for me, there was nobody ahead of me.

I looked back, breathing heavily, with hardly enough strength left to tread water. To my astonishment, the boy was a good ten yards behind.

I waited for him to pass the flag as the pistol cracked. Gently we swam together to the ladder. I gave way to the boy, but he insisted I climb aboard first. Exhausted, we sat together on the bulwark. Though I found it hard to raise a smile as my rival held out his hand, I was glad to grasp it.

HUNTING THE HERRING

THE slur and clack of iron-shod leather thigh boots fill the air
as the fishermen hurry across the Wharf. In the slanting light
of the westering sun their shadows are the shadows of giants.

I clutch my tin under my arm; it has more than enough food
in it: pasty, heavy cake, butter and jam splits. The crew are
already by the punt drawn up above high-water mark.

"Come on lad, we want to be first aweh," Bill shouts.

I dump my tin aboard, grasp the gunwale with the others. Bill
gives the word: "All together, men. Hunchebaw, heave. . . .
Hunchebaw, heave. . . ."

We pull in unison. The keel lifts from its bed of soft sand, sighs
its way down to the water's edge. The punt begins to float off.
We scramble aboard. I put the stubby oar over the stern, scull as
hard as I can to where the *Olive Branch* is moored, the punt
weighed down almost to water level with the seven of us.

From foreshore and quayside other punts waddle out. Soon
there won't be a boat left at her junks.

A billowing cloud of brown smoke rises from Pawlyn's kipper
houses on the Wharf Road facing the harbour. The freshening
breeze brings the smoke across the harbour. My nostrils are filled
with the sharp oak tang of it – October's very essence.

Once aboard the *Olive Branch* we work fast: it's a race to Basset's
Bay seven miles to the nor'west; the herring have been plentiful
there recently.

. Two of the crew cast off the moorings; others unleash the sails.
The halyards creak; up go foresail, mizzen, topsail. Around us,
other crews are as quick as we are: *Bluebell, Clementina, Three
Sisters* are all on the move.

The breeze catches the mizzen topsail. Bill grasps the tiller.
The crew dip long oars over the sides, pull the boat forward.
Once clear of the harbour mouth oars are shipped, sails spring

Once clear of the harbour mouth oars are shipped, sails spring taut and we're away, heeling over, bounding forward.

Only three boats are ahead of us; the sea astern is alive with brown sails, sharp as shark fins. *Three Sisters* is too close-hauled: we have no fear of her. We overtake her, cut past her quarter, reach out toward *Bluebell* and *Clementina*.

The breeze freshens. *Clementina* hauls down her topsail – her skipper never was much of a sailor. As we pass her, I wave contemptuously.

Up through the Sound we sail, smashing through the riptide. *Bluebell* holds her own with us as we leave Godrevy Lighthouse on the starboard. By the time we reach Basset's Bay, *Bluebell* has only her nose in front; we cheer and shout at each other like rival gangs of kids.

The nets are ready to go overboard. We circle a few minutes to choose our ground.

"Shall we try 'ere?" Bill asks.

I cry "Es, 'ere. We're goin' to 'ave a boatload tonight. Dedn't 'ee see the gannets divin'? There's a school of 'errin' 'er, sure 'nuff. They're ours!"

Bill tucks the boat's bow into the wind. The sails are lowered. The nets snake over the lee side, lengthen slackly, swirl, settle.

Bill himself takes first watch. The crew go below; I've already put the kettle on to brew our strong tea. I climb back up the companion-way, trim the riding lights, haul them up the mast head, stay on deck, the wonder of it all still too fresh to be missed.

Darkness sifts down. The boat swings, bow up, stern up – it's like riding on the fairground swing boats I like so much, but without the grinding metallic clash and bump at each end of the swing. . . .

Happy, I listen to the soft thump of the sea against the boat's timbers, the creak of the masts, the complaining of the rigging. I draw the salt air, chill now, deep down into my lungs: I fancy I can smell fish. All around, the riding lights of the fleet glow softly yellow. Above, God lights the stars one by one; they sparkle in the clear air.

The night wind wakens the cold. I'm glad of the two jerseys under my canvas jumper. Glad of the silk scarf – the only one Ma has left – around my throat, the woolly tam on my head.

Time swings by. I climb down the companionway, open my tin, break off a piece of pasty, a lump of heavy cake, fill my tin mug with tea, climb back on deck. I'm hungry; the pasty is savoury, full of beef, liver, onion, potato, turnip, the cake greasy and sweet with figs, the tea strong and sweet.

After a couple of hours, Bill orders me to rouse the men. They come on deck to make the first try of the nets. Leather thigh boots pulled on, long oilskins covering them from neck to knee, they move to the belly of the boat. Three on each side of the net room, they begin to haul. They heave together, heavy work, while I grasp the tiller tightly in sympathy.

The boat net, dark sighing monster, rises, slides dripping over the gunnel, subsides tamely into the net room. The carbide lamps sputter; the sea murmurs, taps at the side of the boat. On the surface of the sea flashes of phosphorescence, brighter by far than the guttering carbide, as bright almost as the stars overhead, rise from bunches of herrings.

Encouraged, the crew haul a little quicker. The moon rises, floods the sea with ghostly light. The boats are black shapes surrounded by silver. Other crews are now hauling; their voices trickle over the water. To me they sound homeless, drained of human warmth, strangely forlorn.

After the boat net, few herring come in. Too soon; we're hauling too soon. We pay out the nets, go below to turn in again. The mate takes over the watch.

Another two hours and an almost empty fleet of nets are hauled.

"Do we try again?" Bill asks.

We agree to try again, five miles to the nor'west to meet the tide as it begins to turn and sweep around the bay. We run up the sails, and away.

Others have the same idea; only a few Weary Willies make for port. The *Vivid* passes us on the larboard quarter. We hail her:

"Any fish?"

"Plenty, but not enough," shouts back her skipper.

Bill nods to the crew, smiles, says "Then there are plenty of fish about. We want them."

We reach our chosen ground, stay on it, don't begin to haul until five o'clock in the morning. No sooner do the crew lay hands on the net than they know there are fish.

The moon thins her light; dawn streaks the sky; the long hard haul goes on.

By a quarter past seven the nets are aboard. Laden with so much fish, they overflow the net room, rise in finny mounds as high as my head above deck.

All the boats we hail have fish. . . . There'll be happy faces in St Ives this morning, money for all to spend . . .

THE DOVE LANE MISSION

EVER restless, ever unsatisfied, Ephraim had in turn been a member of Zion Congregational Chapel, the Plymouth Brethren, Backroads Bible Christian, St Peter's Street New Connexion.

In all these chapels, Ephraim was convinced he knew the Word of God better than anyone else, including the parsons. Had he not been told often enough when he had foreseen some tragic event that he was gifted with second sight?

When Ephraim founded the Dove Lane Mission, his second in command was Paul Tregarthen, owner of the gig *Peace and Plenty*.

A man in the prime of life, Paul was famed for his skill as a fisherman. He fished nearer The Stones, the dangerous reef of rocks stretching from Godrevy Lighthouse westward, than anyone else dared. Often he came back to port with his gig full of herring when other boats returned with few or none.

Last winter, what the Jeremiahs had predicted happened – what those who envied Paul the money he earned *hoped* would happen. A sudden gale drove the gig onto The Stones. Only Paul and his son, Matthew, were picked up out of a crew of five. They would have been drowned, too, if Nicky Toman in *The Nazarene* did not happen to be near enough to see the flare.

Paul's own brother, Ben, was one of the three drowned. As he went away on the black tide, his agonising cry plunged like a dagger into Paul's ears: " 'My God, my God, why hast Thou forsaken me?' "

It was a cry that Paul would hear until his dying day.

Six months passed before Paul was seen again out of doors. As he crossed the Wharf to go and sit on Dobles Wall, it was an old man supporting himself on a stick that the few people about saw, and they could hardly believe their eyes.

They watched Paul as he changed his mind and walked slowly

to the Shamrock Lodge to sit on the seat in front of the Lodge in the sun.

None of the fishermen spoke to him; no one so much as glanced at him; it was as if he were invisible.

On Sunday evening Ephraim arrived at the Dove Lane Mission to find the chapel packed to the very doors. Word had got about that Paul was coming to chapel; his chair at the end of the front row was left vacant for the first time since the disaster.

Everyone waited: eventually Paul came in, shuffled to the front, stick tapping, and sat down. Only Ephraim from his position at the little table facing the congregation spoke to him.

The packed rows of men ignored him: some stared rigidly in front of them; some studied their Bibles or their slim hymn books, compiled and provided by Ephraim, as if they had never seen them before; some seemed deep in prayer.

The service Ephraim led was strained and jerky. His brother Simon pitched the hymns too high; the men had to scrape their throats to reach the high notes. When it came to the sermon, no one could remember Ephraim preaching so badly, so coldly, so disjointedly.

Simon pitched the last hymn so high, few there even attempted to sing it.

The service over, Ephraim made his usual announcement: there would now be a prayer meeting for those who wished to stay. Usually, about a dozen or so of the most devout men would remain; now, to Ephraim's utter astonishment, nobody moved.

Ephraim waited to give them a chance to change their minds, then came from behind the table and, uncertain of himself for once, took his seat in the middle of the front row.

He glanced covertly sideways at Paul. He sat stiffly, motionless, shoulders drawn up protectively, eyes tight shut, face bloodless, lips moving silently.

Still no sound broke the mesmeric silence.

The bare whitewashed walls, the galvanised tin roof, seemed to be pressing in on Ephraim, making him tense his muscles to resist the weight.

The atmosphere was stifling – thick and clotted with emotion. Then one by one the fishermen rose to their feet. Eyes wrinkled tightly closed, hands clasped in front of them, some holding their Bible open between their palms, they prayed aloud. After their customary confession of unworthiness in the sight of the Lord, of sins (unspecified) committed during the past week, they turned their prayers against Paul.

Paul's head sank lower and lower between his shoulders. Ephraim, eyes masked by hands held in front of his face, felt his heart melting in pity, all the more so when he saw blood begin to trickle from Paul's lower lip.

At last Paul could stand it no longer. He lifted his head, fumbled for his stick, which fell rattling on the bare concrete floor. Ephraim's son, Martin, picked it up. As he gave it back, he fleetingly touched Paul's hand: it was icy cold.

After what seemed an age, Paul managed to get to his feet. Turned. Began to grope his way along the white roughcast wall to the door.

"Come back, Paul, my son. Sit down, sit down."

Everyone opened his eyes, saw Ephraim move to help Paul back to his seat.

When he had done so, he turned to face the congregation, wiped the tears streaming down his face, closed his eyes and began to pray.

The voice, when it came from those trembling lips, they hardly recognised: "O living Lord Jesus, look down in mercy on your faithful servant, your loving Paul, here with us this evening. I have sinned, Lord. A minute ago I would have let Paul go into outer darkness again if You had not spoken clearly to me. We have all sinned; Lord Jesus forgive us. . . . The story we spread. Blaming Paul for their deaths. We appointed ourselves judge and jury. We wickedly disobeyed Your Holy word 'Judge not, that ye be not judged.' . . . We judged Paul, Lord. We found him guilty. Six months Paul have not seen the light of day, Lord; our adders' tongues kept him from us. . . . Forgive us our trespasses, O Lord, we pray Thee."

Ephraim's voice died chokingly away. With his palms he wiped his cheeks. He folded his hands once again in front of him, began again to pray. "You told me Paul was innocent, Lord, a revelation a moment ago. You commanded me to proclaim it to these, Your faithful brethren sitting here in Your house. We must welcome Paul back into the fold."

Ephraim opened his eyes, stared at the congregation. He raised his voice; the tone was the familiar one of command. "Look at me, all of you. . . . Paul, my son, come and stand by my side. . . . Let him who is without sin, who dare disobey God's word revealed to me this night, leave now."

Ephraim waited, his blazing eyes fixed on the men huddled together on the hard wooden chairs. No one moved.

Ephraim nodded his satisfaction; the ghost of a smile appeared on his lined face. "Come, then, brothers in Christ, and take Paul's hand. Let him be once more one of the chosen few."

This time Ephraim smiled openly as row after row of black-suited figures rose and began to shuffle sideways into the aisles.

LAUNCHING THE LIFEBOAT

THE sound of the lifeboat maroon woke the whole of Downlong. Before anybody could stir, it went off twice more.

Fully awake, Luke and John sat up in bed; the gusts of wind were so strong, they could feel their bedroom at the exposed back of the house tremble.

"Shall we go, Luke?"

"Es et rainin'?"

"No."

"All right, then, come on."

The gale was blowing so hard by the time they reached the Wharf, they could scarcely stand. Mark, their eldest brother, they knew would already be at the lifeboat house.

First, he'd have tried to grab a life-jacket from the peg. The coxswain would restrain him. Tell him he couldn't be responsible for shipping on one so young: next year, perhaps.

Mark would then line up to be issued with an armband. Nobody was keener on the half-crown paid to those who helped launch the boat and handed in their armband the next day as proof that they actually had.

Soon the rattle of the huge carriage wheels told John and Luke the boat was out of its house and coming along Wharf Road, dragged by upwards of forty panting men on two long ropes.

Mark's fair hair made him easy to pick out in the fitful light of the moon. He was leader on one of the ropes, his tall wiry body bent forward, the end of the rope slung over his shoulder.

Luke turned to his brother. "They've got a rale job on. It's dead law wehter." He pointed at Mark. "'E'll be the first to wade out. 'E'll drown if 'e edn't careful. You d'knaw very well all 'ee think of ez showin' off."

"The tide's just turned, that's somethin'. This northerly gale'll drive the water in all the quicker. . . . I 'ope Mark don't be too rash. Nobody can last more than a second or two in that say; it's all white out there, look. If 'ee do lose 'is footin' and let go the rope, 'ee's a goner. That ground sea will suck 'im under and drag 'im out."

They waited until the lifeboat cleared the narrow slipway, then ran past it over the sand. They stopped on the Cockbank. Looked back. Saw with apprehension how deep the carriage wheels were sinking in the sand; saw, too, how hard the men were toiling to keep them going.

They joined the spectators lining the water's edge, watched with foreboding the two lines of breathless men straining at the ropes.

Mark and Henny on the other rope entered the icy water, waded out until only their head and shoulders were now and again visible above the breakers.

The men on the lines behind them halted, braced themselves as the waves broke against them, submerging them.

Luke said "They'll never get 'er off."

The two lines of men began to divide, keeping the ropes tight. Staggering, but somehow keeping pulling. The lifeboat carriage, stretched at right angles to the shore, was now in the water, the keel of the boat itself awash.

"Well done!" John cried "they're goin' to do et!"

The coxswain gave the signal: the engine roared into life. He leant over the side, pulled the belay pin that released the chain, and the boat slid off her carriage. She met the breakers bow on, was immediately swept sideways. As her keel grounded on sand, she heeled over sharply.

The crew unshipped the long oars. The boys smiled as they saw that their uncle – he was bowman – had his oar in the water first. Together, the crew leaned all their weight on the oars, exerted every ounce of strength to get her afloat.

The men in the water nearest her dropped the ropes, put their back against her bow, pushed as one man. Her bow lifted, swung out to sea. Her keel cleared the sand. Desperately the men kept her going. The twin propellers racing wildly in the air now bit into the water. A shudder, and she was away.

Her bow swung high, crashed down, swung high, crashed down: the stinging, blinding spray swept aboard in sheets, running off the men's yellow oilskins and sou'westers like heavy rain.

A minute more and she cleared the harbour mouth and was gone.

John turned to old Scran on his right. "Knaw what she's after, do 'ee?"

"Two Frenchies, so they seh. Caught in the Channel. Masts gone: no auxiliary engine, they're too neary, so they'll be driftin' fast ashore. Lucky their flares was seen by the coastguard station on Clodgy Point. Goin' ashore out beyond Solavinya, so they calculate. If our boat don't reach them in time, they'll be smashed to matchwood on the rocks. Nobody will be able to get ashore in that say. . . . Our boat wean't be long out. We shall soon knaw."

John clutched Luke's arm. "Down to the Old Quay, then, we got to see'er come back."

BENBOW'S WISH

THE sun stared through Benbow Pollard's bedroom window full upon his face. He woke, yawned, stretched, blinked up at the sky, muttered sleepily: "About half after four by the looks of the sun and as fine a summer mornin' as ever a man clapped eyes on. But I don't knaw as 'ow I'm goin' t'git up fer a minute or two. I'll just turn over and 'ave another – "

"That you wean't, Benbow Pollard." His wife's voice was as scratchy as the elbow she dug thinly into his ribs. "Out you git. I knaw yer tricks, I've summered you and wintered you for more years than I ever want to recollect. Give you 'alf a chance and you'll be fast agen and snorin' like old Betty Berriman's sow. Out you git!"

"Not fer a minute, Edith, dear," Benbow pleaded. "Law water edn't till five o'clock, and I got plenty of time to – "

Edith jerked the bedclothes from him. "Out! You d'knaw as well as I do it'll take you all yer time to dress and git down to Porthmeor Sand to haul yer tackle before the tide turn. And it's gone 'alf-four by my clock, and that's slaw. Time nor tide don't wait for no man, and law tide wean't steh law tide, not even for Benbow Pollard."

Benbow grumbled out of bed, began to dress. "I only 'ope there's plenty of fish. Yesterdeh – "

"Yesterdeh you was too late. Lyin' in bed till the last minute. You've got the slaws, Gospel truth. What they seh about you is right. Even yer own wife 'as to admit et."

"But there wudn't no fish on the tackle when I got down there."

"Because you was too late, I tell you. Somebody had pinched all the fish off your tackle before you got down there – yer cousin, Johnny Salt, most likely. . . ."

Edith jiggled impatiently in bed as Benbow dressed: the squeezed springs whinged; the brass knobs on top of the bedhead chimed bright as a clock.

"Slaw," Edith said, sqinnying down her nose at him: a nose exactly like the beak of Tommy Craze's great rooster down Breakwater, Benbow thought, just as thin and just as yellow. "I've never seen nobody as slaw as you are in all my born days. Slaw — You're too slaw to carry cold denners to a missionary." "Slaw but sure, like old Sam's pony," Benbow muttered, more to himself than to his wife.

Edith snorted. "And old Sam's pony is too slaw to draw a hearse. Slawcoach, you, goest on down, I cean't abide you up 'ere another second."

Benbow stumbled stiffly downstairs, picked up his half-boots from the fender, snatched up his fish basket, opened the door and went out.

The sun, already warm, calmed and soothed him. A lovely summer morning, sure enough. Nobody about yet.

Though he could have gone the shorter way from his house in Teetotal Street down Rope Walk and along Back Road West, through Norway Square to Porthmeor Beach, he walked down to the Wharf for the pleasure of looking at the boats.

The bows in line of the fat-bellied punts were scalloped by the black high-water mark. Beyond and parallel to them, the skiffs lay companionably side by sleek side. Beyond them again were the coloured gigs; and last of all the big mackerel boats, sharp and black.

Dick Legger's *Maid Marion*, the fastest skiff in the harbour: she always won the Regatta, Benbow thought, except last summer when they handicapped her too much; that was old Veale's doing: like a pig in a trough, he had his snitch in everything nowadays.

Next to her was Jan Bennet's *Godrevy*; not a bad little skiff, but she couldn't run before the wind like *Maid Marion*, though; *Maid Marion* could go faster than a tom chasing a she. . . .
— Hullo, Jabez Banfield had painted his skiff red, a bright red! Well, that wouldn't make her sail any faster, red or no red. She lugged herself through the water as if she was towing Jabez's

wife, and she was heavy enough to slow any boat down to a death-march.

Lander Comley's skiff, *Bluebird* - painted blue, of course – was nearly as fast a boat as *Maid Marion*, maybe even better in a light breeze. Blue was a handsome colour for a skiff, the colour of the sea out deep. Nobody but a gentleman like Mr Comley – he kept the shoe shop in Fore Street – would have thought of calling a skiff *Bluebird*, but it suited that skiff well enough, Benbow thought.

Bosanquet's skiff, *Cuttlefish*, was painted two fancy colours; but Bosanquet was a fancy man himself, a fancy one with the women, by all accounts. He'd a hand as soft and smooth as the belly of a ling, a real businessman's hand, and who could stand a chance against a man with a hand like that? Why, Benbow himself had heard Mary, the town moll, say so.

When all was said and done, though, you couldn't beat white for a skiff; white shone like glass on the water in the sun. A white rigged skiff in full canvas was a sight good enough to eat. How he wished – had longed all his days – to own a white skiff; but no such luck. Look at the white skiffs there now: *Clementine*, *Primrose*, *Eastern Shore*, *Shamrock*, *Sea Breeze*, *Catspaw*, *Twin Girls*. . . . Twin Girls! Gascoyne had grizzled enough that time his wife had twins; the fishermen said to his face he was just like that dog with two dicks they'd heard tell of. They mocked him even more when they heard his wife made him change the name of his skiff to *Twin Girls* – serve him right. . . . As for *Catspaw*, who in the name of God would give a skiff a name like that except one of them foreigners – them artist fellows who fought over renting the old pilchard cellars on Porthmeor Sand?

The gilt face of the town clock high up on the tower of the Parish Church accused Benbow. He lifted his arms as if to hug the harbour, then moved slowly on.

At the bottom of Bunkers Hill he stopped again. Ernie White's big cat, Monkey, the biggest cat in all the world, so Ernie claimed, was just tipping over a dung-bucket. It clattered on the cobbles and rolled into the gutter. The cat scrabbled among the contents. "Goest on home, Monkey," said Benbow. "Ernie'll 'ave left 'is front door open all night fer you. 'Ow that drain right under yer nose do fumigate, 'ow we aren't all gassed, beats me . . . Ernie wean't 'ave slept azy last night, thinkin' of you. He'll likely be gettin' ready to go and look fer you this very minute . . . Goest on 'ome."

Benbow continued up Bunkers Hill.

Charlie Ninnes was already out brooming the gutter in front of his house in Love Lane. "A very 'andsome morning', Benbow," he said, cheerful as usual.

"'Andsome, sure 'nuff, Charlie, my son," replied Benbow, and went on his way – no time now to stop and yarn.

He walked briskly across Norway Square, smiling to himself when he saw the door of Number Three, Backroad West, tight shut: Alfred must be still asleep in that bunk of his against the kitchen wall – more coffin than bunk, but that was all right as long as Alfred liked it.

A minute more and Benbow stood looking down onto Porthmeor Beach.

Immediately below high-water mark the sloping sand glowed, newly washed, beige in colour. Farther down, the paler ripples of the sandbars were slashed by long sky-stained pools. Away to the nor'west, Man's Head looked nakedly down on the nook of a cove where Benbow had shot his tackle, a hundred hooks exactly. To the nor'east the Island, St Nicholas's Chapel midway along its spine, flung its forepaws into the shining sea.

A curved-back figure, his overcoats weighty about his knees, was hurrying shoulder-on towards the cove.

"That'll be Man Friday," Benbow said aloud to himself. "I 'ope he d'lave my fish alone this mornin'; mine edn't the only tackle down there. I expect 'ee'll lave mine alone. Poor old Man Friday, no meat in 'es guts, not a crumb. Like a crab goin' to jail, 'e 'ez, 'ee always walk sideways. . . . I'll wait a bit until 'e's finished. No need to make 'aste 'ome, Edith will be snorin' like a grampus

an hour or two yet. I'll see this mornin' if et was Man Friday that
stole my fish yesterdeh. All very well fer Edith to seh et was my
cousin. 'Ow do she knaw? A proper knaw-all she is, do mind
everybody's business except 'er own."

Man Friday was welcome to his bit of whiting. He'd be
famished after sleeping in Simon's carthouse all night, would
clunk down a whiting as quick as a shag.

A new-born breeze ran its silky fingers over Benbow's face. He
sighed: what mortal man had ever clapped eyes on a handsomer
sight than Porthmeor Sand on a blue summer's morning? No
wonder they artist chaps were so keen to have a cellar looking
out on such a fine sight.

He made his stiff way down over the granite steps. The soft
mouths of the milky sand fell sighing away from his plodding
heels. Level with Man 'O War Rock, he noticed that Man Friday
had reached the cove and was humped over the sand. "Must
give'n a chance if 'ee want a bit of my fish," Benbow said. "I'll
set down against the rock 'ere and 'ave a drag on me empty pipe."

He settled into a niche, wriggling his backside until he had
wormed himself a hollow in the white already-warm sand.

He lifted his face, the better to allow the sun to pour its yellow
rays upon it. "Rich, this ez rich. What can a man wish for better
than this?" he asked himself and, forgetting his pipe, fell
deep asleep . . .

Man Friday was having difficulty in getting the whiting off the
hook. He gripped the fish again, dug his blackened fingers into
the silver flesh, thrust the hook down and out through the gills,
savagely tore the gills away as he jerked to free the thin skilvan,
the hook on its end.

He lifted his bushy grey head, the nostrils of his flattened nose
flaring. Good, nobody in sight. His grimed fangs sank into the
whiting's back, tore away the tender juicy flesh. In a few seconds
the flesh was gone from tail to gills, and the rest of the carcass
hidden in the pocket of his outside overcoat. 'Another whiting
or two to take down to Breakwater; boil them up when I'm

boiling the pig meat for Simon,' he thought.

He stooped. This time the barb came away easily from where it had lodged in the gristly underlip. Into the same pocket it went. Just in time - there goating down over the rocks from Man's Head was Dicky Shoe String, his withy basket leaping in his hand.

"Beastly thief," Man Friday muttered, "he'll take all the fish, like he ded yesterdeh." He shambled away, the loose taps of his boots angrily slapping the wet sand.

Benbow in his coloured dream rose lightly from his sand-hugged body. The silver grains hushed under his bare feet; his heels dug momentary graves as he walked. He looked over his shoulder, pleased to see the grains hasten, trickle back, fill in the graves fast as he dug them.

Come to the pebbled, bladder-wracked, corky, coal-dust shelled, feathered and fish-boned high-water mark, he stepped high over it, unwilling to disturb the transient beauty of its looped lace, and struck out printless across the firm mushroom-tinted sand.

It was a good five hundred yards to the cove: he was there in an instant. Around him the rocks flung back the bright javelins of the sun in a froth of fire: under his toes, the grittier shell-sand gleamed. It was the moment of the turning of the tide, so calm that waves small as ripples wandered tiptoe in, dying without breaking.

Benbow, glowing in the grace and ripple and shine of the light, turned reluctantly, went over to his tackle. It was loaded. The fish, leaping lengths of mercury, sputtered and spirted in the shallows.

"They'll fetch a tidy bit of money," he said to his dream self. "This ez my lucky deh. Edith ez goin' to think et's 'er birthdeh. . . . And I shall be able to buy a ounce or two of roll bacca and enjoy a good drag."

Benbow unhooked the fish, threw them in a heap by his basket: blue-tabby mackerel, three fine pollack, a couple of little maiden rays, over a dozen whiting hardly distinguishable from the sand they lay on, a big bass, several flounders brown-backed as mud, four marigold-spotted plaice, a young ling, two shark-toothed congers, and a great portly turbot.

"That theck turbot'll fetch a bob or two," Benbow announced with glee, "and so will – what in the name of 'eaven was that?"

Somebody somewhere in his dream was weeping. Benbow turned round, but could see nothing. "I'm beginnin' to 'ear things in me old age," he muttered. "I thought fer a minute it was Edith come from Man's Head Point up above the cove there and fell down and 'urt 'erself. . . . I could 'ave sworn et was a woman's voice, but I'm mistaken."

Just as he bent to put the fish in the basket, a soft and tearful voice called "Do please come and help me."

"My dear life, you give me quite a turn," Benbow replied. "But of course I'll lend 'ee a 'and. Where are 'ee too, en?"

"At the top of the cove behind this big rock."

"Aw, that's 'ow I couldn't see 'ee. Now 'ow do 'ee come to be be'ind that big rock m'dear, eh? That's a breh foolish – "

"Oh, do please hurry. I've been stuck here since early this morning."

"All right, m'dear, just let me put – "

"Oh, please!"

Benbow dropped the fish he was holding, said hastily "I'll come to once."

He walked up the steeply-sloping sand and rounded the big rock. Behind it, firmly wedged between two smaller rocks, was a mermaid.

"Well, you can scat me down with a feather," said Benbow. "I owe a 'pology to old Jan Trevorrow now sure 'nuff. He always swore he seen one of you that time out Five Points way. Sitting' on a rock in Solavinya Cove she was – singin' and combin' 'er 'air."

The mermaid held out her hands pleadingly, said "Oh, please, do be quick and get me out."

"Old Jan said she 'ad yaller 'air, but yours ez brown. I – "

"We have different colour hair, just as you do. Now – "

"Was you singin' up there on that rock? And combin' - "

"Yes, of course. I ... I ..." The mermaid began to weep bitterly.

"I don't believe you intend to help me."

Benbow, stung into action, sprang forward, seized the mermaid by the tail, pulled, lost his grip, fell backwards, landed with a sousing splash in a pool. Completely drenched, he got up, shook himself, said apologetically, "I cudn't get no purchase on yer tail. Et's as slippery as a mackerel. Just as pretty, too, all blue and green and shinin' like the sea itself ... I'll hale 'ee out by yer 'air, shall I?"

The mermaid shook her little head, held out her hands. "Grip my hands and pull me out."

Benbow grinned shamfacedly. "I forgot," he said. He stooped, gripped the mermaid's tiny cold hands, gently pulled her free. "Well, that's azy done," he said. "Now you can run down to the say, dive in and make yer weh back 'ome."

The mermaid glanced at him despairingly and pointed down. Benbow looked where she was pointing. "Aw, you, I'm as daft as a dumbledory forgettin' you 'ave no feet. Never mind. I'll carry 'ee down to the wehter."

He bent, took the mermaid in his arms: he was amazed how cold she was, and how light. Why, he'd caught many a cod heavier than she was.

At the water's edge the mermaid said "You've been very kind to me. What is your name?"

"Benbow Pollard, but nobody in St Ives wud knaw fer sure who you was talkin' about, unless you called me by my nickname. Everybody Downlong 'ave a nickname. Old Alfred, he paint them pictures they artists like, 'is nickname ez Old Iron – 'ow the childern do tase 'im. My nickname ez Workish. That's becos I never do a 'and's turn unless I cean't 'elp et. ... And my wife" – Benbow lowered his voice, glanced quickly around as if he expected Edith to materialise by his side – "my wife Edith es knawn as The Teetotal Street Terror. When she do give vent you can 'ear 'er all the way up to the Malakoff. And – "

"Yes, yes, that's enough, thank you. I shall call you Benbow,

I like that name."

She paused, seemed to make up her mind. "Now, Benbow, for being so kind to me you can have one wish. Wish for anything you like, and your wish will come true."

" 'Oly mack'rel," Benbow exclaimed, "this ez 'nuff to bate the band!" He looked the mermaid full in her dazzlingly bright eyes. "Sure you're not coddin' me?"

"Sure. Go on, wish. Your wish will come true."

Benbow took out his empty pipe, scratched his grey head with the stem.

After a while, he said "A proper coddle, I don't knaw what to wish for. You see, little maid, they fish I just caught will buy us enough to last the week out, and I shall catch some more another deh, no doubt. So that's the bread and baccy taken care of. So there edn't anythin' – "

"Of course there is." The mermaid sounded quite angry. "Go on, Benbow. Just one wish!"

Anxious to please her but perplexed, Benbow began to shake his head; then suddenly a thought struck him. He bent sideways and whispered in the mermaid's ear.

The mermaid looked at him searchingly, said quietly "Sure Benbow? Are you sure?"

"Sure as Jesus is our Saviour!" Benbow said with utter conviction.

"Then you shall have your wish. . . . Goodbye, and thank you."

Benbow walked waist-deep into the sea.

The mermaid smiled, slipped out of his arms and, with scarcely a ripple, swam out to sea.

Benbow stood for quite a time, as if he could still see her. At last he said forlornly "Goodbye, little maid. Now I realise what I've missed in never bein' lucky enough to 'ave no childern."

What did Benbow wish for in his dream? He never told. And did his wish come true? I don't know. All I do know is that Benbow is now the happiest man in all Downlong, even though they now call him Ben Mermaid. . . .

And Edith? Edith was a changed woman from the day her husband dreamt he met the mermaid. You remember her nickname, The Teetotal Street Terror? Well, now it's The Teetotal Street Dove.

THE BUSKERS, THE BEAR, THE CHEAPJACK, THE TOWN CRIER

The Buskers

THEY came once a fortnight during the summer. They were well liked, and soon a crowd began to gather on the Wharf near the Slipway to hear them.

The man was short, walked with a limp. His shoulder-length hair was fair. Velvet jacket and trousers, green once, had long ago lost almost all their colour. The only bright thing was the plaited band around his neck, from which hung his guitar.

The woman was much taller, her hair even fairer. Cascading over bosom and back, it reached down to the green belt she wore round her slim waist. Her nose was aquiline, her eyes unusually large, intensely blue.

The man took a tin mug from his jacket pocket, filled it from the nearby pump, handed it to the woman. She drank thirstily. He offered her a folded handkerchief. She took it with a smile, carefully unfolded it, wiped her lips, handed it back with a thank you. Only then did he refill the mug and drink himself.

The pair joined hands and walked into the centre of the circle made by the expectant crowd.

The woman sang the songs, the man in his husky voice joining in the choruses. She had a beautiful voice; it sounded like a clear church bell – how I loved to hear it.

Yet it made me feel sad, somehow, filled me with a vague longing I couldn't put a name to.

The woman had been on the stage, they said. Nobody could sing like that who hadn't been trained: they had Ernie White's authority for that, and he should know, he'd sung enough times in the Albert Hall.

It was anybody's guess why she had fallen on such hard times. Who would want to go gadding about the country in all weathers like she had to? Depending on the pence and ha'pence people gave her?

She knew exactly what the listeners wanted and expected; she always sang the same songs.

After each song, she paused; scanned the crowd; smiled with a natural sweetness at them. She lifted her hands, nodded, waited for someone to call out the name of the next song.

She repeated the title loudly and clearly, more for the crowd's benefit, I thought, than for her companion's. He would strum a chord or two, and she would begin to sing, the great rich voice soaring and falling effortlessly.

I used to slip through the crowd after a time and stand at the front. This was because I wanted to be in the best position to see and hear her sing the song she always ended with.

The last time I heard her, she missed the song out. She began to take around the little green velvet bag with the yellow ivory handle. She hadn't even reached the people nearest her before there were shouts begging her to finish with the usual song: I found I had shouted too, though I hadn't realised I had.

"Sorry, ladies and gentlemen, to end with" – her speaking voice was as lovely as her singing voice – "to end with, your favourite and mine."

I always whispered the words to myself as she sang, and a few women joined the man in the chorus.

The last lines were the ones I was waiting for most of all:

> "I dread the dawn
> When I awake and find you gone,
> Ramona, I need you, my own."

I glanced across at Nancy, my childhood sweetheart – she was looking directly at me. When she caught my glance, she smiled a smile as sweet as the woman's.

Was she, I wondered, repeating to herself the sad last lines of the song? For an instant, I thought of her as Ramona . . .

No, no, it didn't fit; I was quite ashamed of myself for being so soppy.

Most of the crowd put something into the woman's little bag. I did not move as they dispersed, but watched the pair as they

disappeared, hand in hand, around the corner and into
Fore Street.

The Bear

THEY came regularly, once a month during the summer, always
on a Saturday when the men were in from the boats and the
women had a bit of time to spare to come out and watch when
the word got around.

I gazed fascinated as the gypsy, behind him a little boy
carrying a hurdy-gurdy, led the bear across the Wharf and onto
the Plat in front of the Slipway. Already, a crowd was gathering.

The gypsy was as dark as Captain Blackie, who they say has
Spanish blood in him. His black curls fizzed out from under his
wide-brimmed, low-crowned black hat. His eyes were as dark as
his face, but glowed as if lit by some inner light. His jet moustache
was long, swept outwards and upwards before turning down
again, just like the wings of a black-backed gull.

Around his thick neck were three strings of coloured beads,
the bottom one with a cross dangling from it. His earrings were
as large as curtain rings; by their colour I was sure they were solid
gold.

His crimson wide-sleeved shirt was open almost to the shiny
brass buckle of the strong leather belt to which the bear's heavy
chain was fastened. The hairs on his chest were as black and
curly as the hair on his head. His brown sleeveless jacket was of
some kind of fur. His leather trousers shone in the bright sun and
were tucked into brown leather boots with yellow patterns on
them.

The bear was big and brown and shaggy, with a sharp-pointed
snout, black as shoe-button eyes. The little bare-footed boy was
as dark as his father, his hair as black, but straight and unkempt.

The boy began to wind the handle of the hurdy-gurdy; the
tune reminded me of the tunes the fairground horses galloped
to, horses I loved to ride. The man stood motionless, waiting for

more people to gather. The bear kept swaying its head and shoulders from side to side, changing its weight from one front paw to another. Its claws, long and black, made a scraping noise on the smooth paving stones.

I gazed at the claws, shuddered inwardly at the bear's slavering jaws, his shaggy coat. Some of the dull-brown fur, I noticed, was missing from his ribs.

Directly across the circle from me was Nancy, my sweetheart, and Mary Stevens, the one girl in our class I didn't like. Mary was tugging at Nancy's elbow; she pointed at the boy, who had stopped playing, the hurdy-gurdy balanced on its pole, he ready to turn the handle again.

Nancy gestured; I shook my head vigorously; I didn't want the two of them joining me.

The gypsy raised his whip, cracked it in the air. At once the bear raised itself on its hind legs; it was much taller than its master. Another crack of the whip and the bear began to dance to the sound of the hurdy-gurdy.

The crowd clapped. The gypsy smiled, his teeth white as a gull's breast against his dark skin.

The bear bobbed up and down in time to the music, its front paws held up like a dog begging. I half expected it to fall over backwards, it looked so clumsy. Every time it dropped down on its four paws, its master flicked it with the whip and it heaved upright again, emitting a sound more like a soft groan than anything else.

Each time the bear reared up, the crowd began clapping: they were obviously reluctant for the show to end.

When the little boy carefully rested the hurdy-gurdy on the ground and went around with the bag, I was pleased to see he took up a better collection than in Da's Zion Congregational Chapel many a Sunday.

The crowd began to disperse. Suddenly Mary Stevens – she would! – darted forward, her hand stretched out to touch the bear's snout. The bear sprang to meet her. The gypsy shouted, braced his whole weight back, pulled with all his strength on the chain to check the beast.

At the same instant, the boy jumped in front of Mary, shoved her so roughly that she fell backwards. The boy ignored her, stooped, picked up the hurdy-gurdy, turned the handle a few times to ascertain it still played.

I watched Mary Stevens pick herself up and walk back to join Nancy. She looked as pleased with herself as if she had done something to be proud of.

That's Mary for you, I thought, she's got dish water for brains. If that bear had got his claws in her, he would have torn her to shreds — serve her right!

The Cheapjack

WHEN the cheapjack, Pat Webster, came to the Wharf, he usually attracted more people than either the buskers or the gypsy with his bear.

Doubtless, this was because he always was so entertaining — better than a peepshow, even better than the old bearded man's Punch and Judy, that was the general opinion.

After he had set up his stall and laid out his goods: stockings, socks, boots, shoes, men and women's underwear (you can imagine what fun he had displaying these), cheap jewellery, watches, alarm clocks; in fact, almost everything under the sun you could use in the house or put on your back — he always began with the same trick.

He held up three watches, put them carefully into three bags.

He criss-crossed the bags to and fro, took a hammer and smashed it down again and again on one of the bags. At the sound of breaking glass and metal, the sort of sound a watch being smashed to pieces would surely make, a slight shudder ran through the crowd: to destroy such a precious thing as a watch!

Everyone waited tensely, a few emitting nervous titters. Though we all had seen the trick many times before, we were never tired of hoping that this time the trick had gone wrong and

Pat had really smashed a watch to pieces: we would have loved to see the expression on his round, florid face if he had.

Pat, sleeves rolled up — "Nothin' up my sleeves except my arms, ladies, gen'lemen" — winked, his smooth, fat cheeks creased in a broad smile, his little eyes bright with mischief, his nicotine-stained teeth bared, his nose glowing like the red light in the lighthouse on the end of Smeaton's Pier.

He knew to a second when he should proceed. He laughed, a great rollicking laugh he could turn on like a tap, held up the bags one after the other, shook each one. No sound: no sound whatsoever. Disappointed though some were, we all waited eagerly for him to produce the watches from the bags. Intact, of course, held dangling in front of our eyes, their chains shining in the sun, the utterly baffling trick performed once again.

These were the three watches he auctioned first, beginning with an impossibly high price and coming down step by step each time he banged his gavel.

When he'd reached his intended price, the result of this charade was to convince his customers that they were getting a real bargain.

Every so often, as he described in glowing terms whatever he was attempting to sell, he would come out with the phrase everybody was waiting for, to be greeted with a laugh: "There you are, lady, cheap enough to throw at the cat to make the baby laugh!"

He always did a roaring trade. We all would go away, those who had bought and those who hadn't, smiling, assured — and how right we were! — that never had there been, nor ever would be, a cheapjack like our very own honest (to use his own favourite word about himself) Pat Webster.

The Town Crier

"'ERE come A'bram, look. Gather round, let's 'ave a bit of a maygame wid'n."

The fishermen gladly obey, just as eager to dangle in front of Abraham the stale-baited hook they know he will take, no matter how many times it is offered.

Abraham slouches forward, his long red cloak sweeping the ground. He stops in the middle of the Plat, wipes his mouth with the back of his hand, begins to ring his bell, stops ringing, shouts "Oyeez, Oye − "

"'Old 'ard, Ab'ram, my 'andsome, you've forgot to put on yer cocked 'at, ez under yer arm, look. You cean't do yer oyez without yer three-cornered 'at now, can 'ee?"

Abraham lifts his clown's white face, lips trembling, rheumy eyes glancing momentarily at his tormentors. He hears the titters of the bystanders, puts on the ceremonial hat, savagely rings the big bell, cries hoarsely "Oyeez, oyeez, oyeez, lost stolen or strayed, white kitten with black − "

"A'bram, old 'ard a minute, my son, 'ang on. Louder, if you plaze. Sure as my Maker's above, I cean't make out a single word. Somebody got bitten , did 'ee seh? Who bit who, tell me, my son?"

Fidgeting, blinking, Abraham stands at bay in the ring and rasps his breath. This time he'll make his announcement, even if Satan Himself stands in the door − a bob hard earned.

The job done, he clutches the big bell by the clapper.

He tucks the hat again under his arm. Head bent, he shuffles quivering away, looks neither to right not left. The burden of all his frustrated years lies heavy as sin on his stooped shoulders, rightful place among his townsfolk denied.

Out of sight in Bethesda Hill he stops and looks about him: nobody in sight. Then from white cheeks and hollow eyes, he knuckles bitter, inconsolable tears.

ARTISTS' SHOW DAY

S cene: Norway Square. Characters: six women from Norway Square, Love Lane and Virgin Street. Ellen, Louie and Bessie are best-changed; Martha, Lizzie and Rachel are in pinnies, the two former, brooms in hand.

Ellen: We've just come from the studios. Aren't 'ee goin', en?
Lizzie (leaning on her broom) : We're in two minds, Martha and me.
Rachel : No, I edn't goin'. Last year trailin' all that way down Ropewalk, then climbin' they steep wood steps —
Louie : Ladders, more like.
Rachel : 'Es, you, ladders, sure 'nuff. Well, climbin' them ladders last year up to they old fishermen's lofts they artists use as studios, give me the gyp. All on fire, my rickety old knees was. And shaky too, them ladders. The Lord above knaw how old they are. Somebody is goin' to kill 'issell one of these fine dehs. Mark my word! Why they artists wanted to buy they old lofts to pehnt in, I shall never fathom.
Ellen: Don't be so fulish, maid. Fer the light shinin' in off Meor Say all the weh from America. The best light in the world and —
Louie: Thee'rt right, maid. I've heerd Cap'n Smart seh so, and John Park, too, many's the time.
Ellen : This year ez much better. By far. You ought to go. Commander Bradshaw's studio is full of they great pictures of sailin' vessels in rough says. Rich, you! 'Ee do knaw what they gee four masters look like in they gee waves. Far more than some I cud mention.
Bessie: So do Mr Olsson. That one with moonlight on the say. You've never seen anything like et. You cud just as well be there lookin' at et, only it's better than the rale thing. Who can paint moonlight shinin' on the wehter better than 'ee? Like Paradise.
Martha and Lizzie nod their agreement, look at each other questioningly.

67

Ellen : Then there's Borlase Smart. Smart be name, smart be nature. Always clane and tidy, shoes and glasses gleamin' like old Bill's glass eye in the sun. Straight as a mast; 'ee must have a broomstick down his back. Jailin' along, left right, left right, walkin' stick swinging'. Still like the soldier 'ee used to be. Not like some of they artists, more like dung 'eaps than anythin' else. 'Ee can draw, Cap'n Smart can. You can meak out everything that's in the picture. Clear as deh. Better than a photo.

Lizzie : And John Park. We mustn't ferget old John. Nobody more friendly than 'ee. Why, 'ee cud be a St Ives man, but we do knaw they're all foreigners except Peter Lanyon, and 'ee's one of we. An' what a 'an'some young man 'ee ez!

Ellen : An' don' fergit Ben Nicholson's studio. 'Ee –

Louie : Ben! I do dearly love to see Ben passin' my door with 'is little black cap and fisherman's jersey up. Lookin' over 'is shoulder now and agen as if Satan 'isself was after 'im. Jailin' along like a little lad.

Lizzie : Well, as I was sayin' before you poked your oar in, Louie, as good as a pleh they pictures in Ben's studio, but I don't call *them* pictures. All them white and greh and yallah squares and circles. And they little boats 'ee's started drawin'. I'd rather look at old Alfred's, I rarely wud. Any'ow, Alfred's another St Ives artist, if you can call 'ee a artist, edn't 'ee?

Martha (tartly) : Of course 'ee edn't. 'Ow can 'ee be so peasy-brained, maid? 'Ee's a Devon man born and bred. I thought everybody do knaw that.

Lizzie : Shall we drop tools an' go, then, Martha?

Martha (uncertainly) : Well, I don' knaw. I've still got they pilchards to marinate for Mr Quick. 'Ee do dearly love a mallio.

Ellen (scornfully) : Aw, 'ee can weht. Goest on, both of you. And mind you don't miss what's in Number One.

Martha : Number One? That's old Slade's studio, edn't it? Last year 'ee 'ad fifty or sixty paintin's of I don't knaw what. Blobs of paint so theck, all colours of the rainbow, so theck 'ee must 'ave used a trowel. Take that monstrous one, for instance. Against the back wall, et was. If 'ee ever sell et, et'll 'ave to go out through the front winders and be lowered down to Meor Sand with pulley and tackle. Et'll take all 'ands on deck, et'll cost 'im a fortune. . . . An' what was on et! All them blobs mixed together. *Sky and Say* he called et. Give me a few pots of boat's paint to dab over a gig's mizzen and I cud do better. . . . But what's Slade got this year?

Ellen : More blobs of paint; it look like the same boat's paint as Old Alfred do use, but this time you can make out what they are. Women naked as the deh they was born, my dear life, you'd never credit it. All shapes and sizes, you've never seen the like, you cean't keep a straight face. Better than Punch and Judy. Goest on, I tell 'ee.

Lizzie (nudging Martha) : Come on, maid. I ralely do enjoy Artists' Shaw Deh. Et's our only chance to see the pictures. I cean't miss them Bradshaws and that moonlight. An' we wean't fergit old Slade, never you fret, Ellen. Who knaws, we might bump into our 'usbands there, caps down over their eyes, a bit of disguise or to see better, I don't knaw which. No use them swearin' blind either they wudn't there. Men! We'll give them ballyraggin' sure 'nuff. They wean't be able to lift their 'eads or look us in the eye for dehs.

TONGUES

"**W**HERE in the name of God do 'ee git the money from? A humbug like 'is feyther before 'n. A pair of dirty robbers. Steal the eyes out of a statue. Lawyers! Diddled more people Downlong out of their 'ouses than I've got fingers on my two 'ands.

" – 'E's left 'er agen. Third time this year. Per'aps 'e'll 'ave the guts to steh aweh this time. Who cud live with a woman with a tongue more full of p'ison than a serpent's?"

" – Janie? She's frightened, m' dear. Marriage to that soft dumbledory in the Town 'All 'as frightened 'er. Grand as yer 'at, and twice as fancy. 'Eard 'er open 'er trap lately, 'ave 'ee? Tryin' to talk Uplong, but steppin' right back in et all the time. Her nose so 'igh in the air you'd think she 'ad cat shit under it. In that noo coat of 'ers – the second one this year! – her backside stick out that far you cud leh a tay party for two on et."

" – 'Ere come Trenowden, the mayor. With 'is 'ard hat on. I wonder 'ee don't melt in the 'eat – and 'is patent leather shoes, you can see yer picture in them. I like to see that Dick Turpin 'at on that bald-as-a-badger's-ass 'ead of 'is, they furry robes and that gee chain. 'Ardly enuff strength to stand up in them. No wonder when you think of what 'ee git up to with all 'is fancy women."

" – Did 'ee see what 'appened down the Wharf yesterdeh? No? Well, I ded right under Bethesda 'Ill wall. Well, that artist fellah, Stanley . . . Stanley Spencer, that's et. Little felleh lookin' 'alf starved, them gee glasses nearly bigger than 'is chacks. There 'ee was right under the wall, 'is easel perched up higher than 'isself and a gee picture on et. Beside 'im a woman twice as tall and thin as a shotten 'errin', her dress all flowers 'angin' down to 'er feet, toes pokin' out underneath, an' a sun 'at big as a dung bucket lid

70

wi' raffia flowers on et. 'Et was a scorchin' 'ot deh, as you do knaw, the sun beaten' down, you could fry fish on top of the granite wall, an' 'ee stripped off with no shirt on an' 'is trousers angin' from 'is bracers, the waist so big you cud lean over the wall an' look right down an' see all 'is trinklements. . . . Well, Mamie Broad, you do knaw what she's like - alwehs was an' alwehs will be — she took up the rope mat she was baten' and dabbed et down over the wall right down on the easel, artist an' all. . . . All Bedlam broke loose. I dedn't stop to see the upshot. I jailed up Bethesda 'ill as fast as my two poor old trotters cud carry me. . . . When all is said an' done Mamie needn't 'ave done that, but that's Mamie for 'ee, m'dear. The talk of Downlong growin' up, an' still the talk of Downlong now she's old enuff to knaw better. . . . Poor old chap, I felt ralely sorry for 'm."

" — Just seen Willie Care up on the roof of No. 3, Back Road West. Lowerin' a gee stone down Alfred's chimbley. To drive aweh the voices Alfred do 'ear in the night. Voices of Old Nick 'isself, he seh, or evil spirits; he do change 'is tune, dependin' on 'ow 'ee is feelin', daft old soul. Et was only 'is wife, Susan Agland, kept 'im in 'is right mind. Old enuff to be 'is mawther, and that was what she was to 'n. But I don't think it's right fer them boys to t'ase the life out ob'm as they do. What 'ave we got the police for, anyweh? They boys, livin' devils they are, tippin' up 'is dung bucket right on 'is doorstep. They do that to everybody when they're playin' one of their games, but Alfred, silly old fool, think they only do et to 'im. Bobbin' stones at his front door, now and then too, so he seh. No wonder the poor old fellah think they're prosecutin' 'im, 'ave bin sent by one of they demons whose voices 'e's always 'arken to comin' down the chimbley."

" — Grievin', ez she? She's no more grievin' than my Sunday 'at. Mark my words. 'E'll 'ardly 'ave gone cold in ez greave before she's got another man by the ass, or my name edn't Lizzie Giles."

" — Faithful unto death, that's Mary, me dear, not like some we cud neame. Still in black she ez three years after 'er Bill went to join 'is Maker in 'eaven above. Will never 'ave another coloured garment to 'er back as long as she's goin' through this vale of tears, that's what she swear. Every blessèd night of 'er life, kneelin' at the foot of their bed prayin' for Bill, like they used to do together prayin' for one another. Keep 'is 'at 'ung on the peg be'ind the front door she do, where 'ee used to 'ang et when 'ee come 'ome from work. Bald as a egg 'ee was, seemed ashamed of et as 'ee was only a young man, so 'ee was never seen without 'is 'at, come rain, come shine. Mary swear she'll keep et in ets rightful place on that peg until 'er dyin' deh. As good as they statues they worship up Tregenna Hill in that Catholic Church. Full of graven images et ez, so they seh, but I've never set foot in et, nor intend to. . . . Faithful until death, Mary ez, m'dear, faithful unto death. I do commend 'er. I commend 'er with all my 'eart and soul."

DESECRATION OF THE SABBATH

T HE following Sunday at two o'clock exactly, just when the children were going to Sunday School, the Irishman unmoored his boat.

The sound of the two great engines starting up shattered the Sabbath peace, dinned in the fishermen's ears as they sat in front of the two lodges quietly smoking and yarning. It brought the women to their doors to have their say about the cusséd foreigner.

The fishermen rose as one man. . . . So he *was* taking the craft out again on the Sabbath! Although he had kept her moored up last Sunday, it was now obvious that neither Simon nor any of the other chapel elders had convinced him – as they thought they had – not to take the boat out.

It was a mortal sin to desecrate the Sabbath in this way. The Irishman knew very well what they believed, how they felt: 'Six days shalt thou labour, and on the seventh take thy rest'. They had always kept God's commandment. Nobody had ever dared take a boat out on the Sabbath day, let alone go fishing in it.

In righteous silence they stood watching. The big red craft motored slowly out of the harbour mouth. Red, in heaven's name: her very colour was an insult!

Where was he going to cast his lines? Right where they could see him; that's what he had done before. He wanted to make quite sure they all knew what he was doing – to give the greatest offence.

Instead of heading out into the bay as they expected, he steered east to Pednolva Point. From the hotel there he took on board two women and a man.

First he swept across Porthminster Beach, the zoom-zoom of the motors thrown back from the cliff.

The fishermen shuffled their feet, gnawed at their pipe stems in helpless anger. Despite themselves, they could not take their eyes off the big craft.

All that long afternoon the Irishman kept the boat going, ploughing from Porthminster Point across the harbour mouth to Porthgwidden Beach, to and fro, to and fro.

Word spread like wildfire that something – nobody knew what – was going to happen. Soon the Wharf road fronting the harbour was crowded with men, women and children.

They stood there watching the boat; they listened to the racket of its engines; they muttered amongst themselves as their sense of desecration grew. This foreigner represented all the evil forces from the outside world that were threatening their traditional way of life, the values they held most sacred. He was, they believed, challenging God Himself.

Godless violator! He must be driven away. By whatever means: God would sanction and bless whatever had to be done.

Above the buzz of talk, some voices were raised in threat.

Suddenly there was silence; the big red craft, colour of blood, was coming into harbour; only the Irishman was aboard. She slackened speed as she cruised through the harbour mouth.

A surge of expectancy, frightening in its intensity, ran through the crowd as the Irishman headed straight for the steps. . . . Was he going to tie up at the steps? Come ashore? Did he dare? If he did . . .

At the very last moment the Irishman altered course, steered quietly to mid-harbour, picked up his junks, slowly made fast bow and stern ropes, stowed everything shipshape, straightened, stretched, arms bent, elbows braced back, great chest expanded, fist clenched.

He relaxed, stook astraddle facing the crowd, his white teeth bared in a contemptuous grin. He dug his hands into his pockets and hunched his great shoulders. He raised one big hand, pushed back a lock of black hair from his forehead, slowly scratched a nose bashed flat on his dark-skinned face. Again he lifted his arms, clenched his big biceps.

"What the hell are ye waitin' for to see?" he yelled.

Immediately the crowd found voice. Shouts told him to cast off his accurséd boat and get out of port. Now. At once. Voices warned him that if he did not, it would be more than his life was worth to put foot ashore. He would never break another Sabbath in St Ives.

A woman's voice, shrill with blood lust, rose above the din: "Set foot ashore, Satan you, and we'll claw you to pieces!"

The Irishman's face contorted with rage. He lifted his head, squared his wide shoulders.

"To hell wi' ye and yer Sabbath," he shouted. "Nobody is goin' to run me out of port. I can beat any one of ye in fair foight. Give me fair play. I'll take on as many of ye as come forward. One at a toime. There isn't a man among ye dare face me."

The cheer this fetched from a group of youngsters was followed by a baffled silence.

The Irishman nodded his head in satisfaction. He turned from side to side to scan the crowd, grinned mockingly.

A moment more and the silence was broken by a quiet voice: "I'm comin' out to 'ee, me son."

The crowd parted willingly as Joel made his way down over the steps. They watched him with sinking hearts as he carefully folded his best Sunday jacket and put it over the rail. Yes, Joel was the strongest man Downlong, or had been in his youth, despite his small size – God's strength to do God's work, Foolish Georgie used to say – but to face this giant, well, they feared for him. Talk about David and Goliath, well, all they could do now was to pray for him.

Joel stumbled as he put his foot on the gunwale of a punt, retrieved his balance, hopped safely down on the duck boards.

"Cast 'er off," he said.

Someone undid the painter, threw the rope aboard, watched as Joel sculled gently towards the Irishman.

The Irishman stared. The man in the punt was small. Old, too. And clumsy. What did this mean? Was it some trick?

No good, though, taking chances. He tensed, adjusted his stance, legs slightly apart, long arms held away from his sides, formidable fists clenched.

As Joel stepped across into the belly of the speedboat, the

Irishman hit him before he found a proper foothold.

The sharp crack of the blow ricochetted against the granite harbour wall.

Joel fell to the bottom of the boat as if poleaxed.

Grinning savagely, the Irishman hit Joel again as he was rising shakily to his feet. The second blow landed on Joel's temple, drawing blood, and again he fell with a crash.

The crowd expelled its breath in a defeated sigh. Satan had beaten their champion. So easily. Without Joel striking a single blow. But what did they expect? A miracle? The age of miracles was long past.

They could not believe their eyes as they saw Joel get up once more.

Calmly the Irishman measured his distance. The punch, this time to the point of the jaw, would put paid to an opponent he now respected – but what had to be done had to be done.

The Irishman launched the finishing blow. Joel ducked instinctively. Off balance, the Irishman lurched forward. Joel's arms whipped around his ribs. The Irishman grunted as their bodies collided with a dull thump.

The Irishman found himself lifted off his feet. Desperately, head strained back with effort, he clawed at the arms clamped around him.

Joel pressed his face against his opponent's collar bone. Exerted more pressure . . .

The Irishman panicked. His face whitened in agony as he felt his ribs coming together. His mouth gaped open. He fought for breath. Grabbed Joel's hair to pull his head away – in vain.

Face turning purple, eyes bulging, the Irishman's arms twitched like the wings of a newly-killed chicken . . . A minute more and they dropped limply to his side. His whole body sagged, head lolling sideways.

Joel released him. Grasped him by the collar and crotch. Swung him to chest level. Paused, gathering all his strength, then jerked him high above his head and held him suspended there.

The Irishman's legs and arms jerked feebly. He screamed as

the welcome air rushed into his starved lungs. Then Joel with all his force flung him down into the bottom of the boat.

The sound reverberated over the water and mingled with the low hissing of released breath as the spectators relaxed their tensed bodies. They were quite sure the Satan would not rise for more.

Utterly exhausted, the blood mingling with the sweat that ran from his forehead, Joel sat on the gunwale, elbows on knees, head resting in his hands. Everyone knew he was praying, and many followed suit.

Prayer finished, Joel threw a bailer of water over the head of the man lying inert at his feet. Another bailer, and the Irishman sat up, shaking his tousled head from side to side.

Joel leaned over him, spoke so quietly no one could hear what he was saying. He waited until the Irishman nodded before he climbed back into the punt, sat on a thwart and waited

The Irishman rubbed his eyes, rose unsteadily to his feet, cast off his moorings, started his big outboard motors. Without lifting his head to look at Joel or the crowd, he steered out to sea.

It was as if the church clock striking four was the signal some were waiting for.

A voice cried "The café! Another foreigner. We must make a clean sweep today. The town hall give 'en permission to open on a Sunday, just to suit they gentry that stay in the hotels. Now's the time to put a stop to Sabbath breakin'. Come on, lads!"

The gang of youngsters who had cheered the Irishman led the rush. Though most were not prepared to take a hand in anything, they wanted to see what was done.

A weighing machine in front of the café was whisked into the air and hurled through the front window. Boots battered the advertisement boards to bits.

The youngsters were by now inside. They swung chairs like battle-axes against the long wall mirrors. They overturned tables, jumped on them until they splintered into matchwood. They ripped out the till; its drawers jangled open; the money splashed down, was picked up by greedy hands. The sturdy bar was uprooted, pulled sideways to the floor, stamped on savagely until it disintegrated. Fortunately, the terror-stricken proprietor had long since disappeared.

For many who approved wholeheartedly in facing down the Irishman, the riot in the café came as a profound shock.

That Sunday evening, in the small chapels set up and run by themselves, prayers were offered to ask God's forgiveness for what had happened.

Simon, who had been informed that his sons had been in the thick of the fray, in particular bore a heavy burden of guilt. In his prayer in front of the congregation, he affirmed they were no sons of his. His voice broke as he added "The Good Book is right. I have nourished and brought up children, and they have rebelled against me to bring down my gray hairs in sorrow to the grave. Until they come and confess their sins openly before our congregation, I disown them. They are no sons of mine."

But his sons never did come.

They knew, if their father did not, that the old way of life was changing, would soon be gone for ever.

ANDREW

ANDREW stuck out his lower lip, blew upwards at an imaginary moustache. "Look, Ma, Here's Da preachin' a sermon in Bible Christian Chapel." He imitated his father's voice exactly. "And the Lord said unto Moses, Come forth, and he come fifth and got the sixth prize."

His mother's huge body jellied into laughter. She choked on the piece of beef she was swallowing: her face purpled. She retched, tongue protruding. With a convulsive effort, she coughed up the beef, spat it into the palm of her hand, threw it into the grate. She lifted her pinny and wiped the spittle from her chin.

"You'll chuk me yet. If that piece of beef 'ad stuck in me gullet, I'd 'ave chuked," she gasped. "What yer feyther wud say if he saw you mockin' 'im, 'ed pull yer ears longer than rabbits' ears. . . . And 'ere I sit laughin' at you like a tomfool with no more sense to me than Jan Pearce's dunkey that time that went to drink out of the well and fell in and broke 'is neck. . . . Feyther wud never forgive me if 'e saw me."

Andrew, pleased with the effect of his drollery, repeated the joke.

Mrs Richards began to laugh again, unrestrained and childlike: she laughed as easily and frequently in these latter years as she gave way to fits of sudden and uncontrollable anger.

Andrew reverted to a trick he used to play on her when he was little. He had no idea what made him do it now, he hadn't done it for years. He jumped forward, slipped his fingers beneath her enormous double chin, shook the flesh to and fro. At the same time, he hooked the forefinger of his other hand under the end of her well-worn corset, then let it go with a twang against her mountainous belly.

"Do stop. In the name of all that's above, do stop, Andrew. What a devilskin thee art. There was never a more 'ardened aggravator than thee. Goest on down to the bakehouse to yer feyther and lave me in peace."

"And he come fifth and got the sixth prize," Andrew sang out. "Lave me alone. You're to big to be doin' this now, it edn't dacent. And you're 'urtin' me. Lave me alone, I tell 'ee!" The boy should have been warned by the new note in his mother's voice, and by the sudden rush of colour to her fat cheeks. He persisted, however, chanting the phrase again and again; and each time, he shook her double chin and twanged the corset.

Suddenly she pushed him away, seized the breadknife, struck him a swinging blow on the side of the face with the flat of the blade. "Aggravatin' morgay!" she shouted, "you've got the Devil in you todeh. Now will you stop!"

The stinging impact of the blow made Andrew think his face was gashed: he cried out more in fear than pain. Tears filled his eyes; he could not see if his fingers were covered in blood or not as he took them from his cheek.

Contritely Mrs Richards dropped the knife. She leaned her gross weight forward and reached out for him. He jumped back from her and ran through the door.

Motionless, his mother heard his bare feet sputter down the granite steps, out through the lane past the bakehouse door and into Fore Street. Her eyes glazed over and she said in a small child's voice "I didn't mane to strike you, Andrew, I didn't mane to; I don't knaw what come over me."

Andrew stopped in Fore Street and wiped the tears away on the cuff of his jersey. The blow from the knife had hurt like fire.

The harbour when he reached it was quiet beneath the brightness of the early-afternoon sun. Three cats were curled asleep on the edge of the little sea wall. A gull stood drowsily a few paces farther along. The tide was in, must just have turned; it was making a different sound. At the water's edge a pair of gulls, wings raised and necks convulsively stretched, fought a tug-of-war over the dead body of a ray. A black-backed gull swooped in on them, drove them off. He jabbed indifferently at the ray, the unflawed white of his predatory head brilliant above the ebony sheen of his wings, before stalking away.

"You're too big for yer boots, that's what's the matter with you, you didn't want that ray at all, you only wanted to show you're boss, like my big brother," Andrew said.

A small black object caught his attention. He jumped down and ran over the sand to where it was. It lay in a loop of the tidemark among the rest of the debris: bits of cork and wood, empty shells, fishbones and seaweed, little yellow balls of excrement that stank in the heat of the sun.

Andrew squatted, gently touched the tiny body stretched in the casual crudity of death. The eyes of the drowned kitten were wide open, questioning what had happened. Its bared teeth were fine and white as herring bones. The tip of the minute pink tongue was curled as if about to lap.

Acting on a sudden impulse, he seized the body by its tail and threw it back into the sea. It splashed heavily and sank at once. In a moment it reappeared, but only part of the grotesquely-swollen belly remained above the calm surface.

He thought 'I am a fool. I wish now I'd dug a soft grave in the sand and buried it. That's what I should like if I was dead, a soft warm grave.'

He recalled his original intention and headed for Breakwater. He toiled across the loose milky sand. As he hurried up Bethesda Hill, he began to sweat.

Andrew's first act when he reached Breakwater was to let out his pigeons, well over a score of them. They rose and gathered at once in a tight flock, the sound of their wings dry and sharp as lobsters struggling in a withy basket, then swept higher to begin their flight. They wheeled across Porthgwidden Beach, their bodies merging into the green slope at the back of the Island before they headed swiftly out to sea, glinting like legendary birds. Making for home, they became silhouettes between the watcher and the sun, bereft momentarily of their bright beauty. Eventually they swerved in past Merren Rock, dipped as if in salute of their loft, then began at once the second ellipse of their ecstatic flight.

Andrew was watching them as if he were seeing them for the very first time. "My 'andsome pigeons," he said softly, "I wish I was up there with you; I wish sometimes I wudn't a boy at all. Ma say I was changed in the cradle; I'm not like all my other brothers. All she and they do is to boss me about. I wish I believed in 'eaven. That wud be 'eaven fer me up there with my pigeons. I wudn't mind dyin' now if that's what I cud do."

He touched the bruise on his cheek. Perhaps Ma had struck him harder than she intended, but that didn't make the bruise go away . . . and his brothers were always fighting: how sick of it all he was.

The zigzag path behind the pigeon loft led steeply down to the sand below. Andrew went down, began to scramble over the huge sea-coloured boulders, stopping now and again to put his face against their sea-smooth warm surfaces, then worked his way seaward to the largest of all the pools.

He reached it, sat down against a rock facing the sun. He closed his eyes and sighed. There wasn't only Ma and his brothers, there was Da as well. He seemed more stern than ever. And Sunday School every Sunday afternoon, chapel every Sunday evening. Why did Da always have to drag him along? Because he was still too young to defy him, like the others had already done, that's why. Well, the time would come. It wouldn't be so bad if the preachers didn't preach hell fire and damnation all the time. And Da was as bad as all the others, if not worse, when it was his turn to preach.

Andrew could not prevent himself from shivering. No wonder he'd been afraid of the dark when he was small: hell was dark, even though it was a fiery pit. No wonder he was afraid at times still – felt the skin on the back of his neck and all the way down his spine tingling, as if some horrible thing was behind him, menacing him. . . . And the nightmares. Well, at least he didn't have nightmares about hell any more, that was something.

He got up, stood looking down, down into the silent world of the pool; he knew that in a moment it would put its familiar spell on him. No matter how many times he came here, it always did. He imagined he was in the pool, the seaweed soft and cool as shadows, swimming among the shrimps and blennies, and sharing for ever their secret life.

As last he shook himself out of his daydream, grabbed a stone, knocked a limpet from the rock, with his thumb gouged it out from its shell. He tied the limpet to a piece of string, squatted on the lip of the pool and lowered it gently into the water. It touched bottom. Instantly a crab pranced sideways from its hiding place and seized the bait.

"You must be the biggest fool of all, you'll never learn. If I've caught you once like this, I've caught you dozens of times. Don't let go, greedy guts."

He hauled up the string as he spoke. He was careful not to jerk or allow the crab to bump against the side of the rock, for fear of dislodging it. He swung the crab onto the rock where he was standing. It was a large fiddler crab, its shell covered in short fine hair, mousey in colour.

As the crab touched the rock, it dropped the bait, lurched back on its shell, held its nippers in front of it ready for attack or defence.

"No good you wavin' they pinchey-paws at me. I've a good mind to turn you over on yer back and lave you there till you're dead. You never seem to get any friendlier, no matter 'ow many times I catch you." He bent down until he could look into the crab's bright-red eyes. "King of the pool, silly old fool, you're as daft as Jan Pearce's old dunkey; you'll never learn."

He jerked the bait from the string, dropped it into the pool directly in front of the crab's hideout. He moved round behind the crab and picked it up. He stroked the soft hair on its shell for an instant, then stooped and let the crab sink downwards over the bait.

"You're not much company, but you deserve yer feed, old bustguts, you."

The crab snatched the bait the second it grounded and hurried with it into the crevice in the rock.

Andrew stood staring at the place where the crab had disappeared, and now there were tears in his eyes. "It's all right fer you, its always all right fer you. Nobody to bother you down there. And even if there was, you've always got somewhere you can go and hide. Not like me – I 'aven't got nowhere."

TEACHERS

Miss Hicks and Miss Pearce

MISS Hicks came to school on a motorbike – how we infants stared! – an unheard-of thing.

She wore grey breeches, a thick grey belted jacket, greeny stockings and brown boots. Her hair was ginger; and ginger was her temper. Big hands red and raw as freshly-cut meat; she was a farmer's daughter, with a voice as rough as rust.

She had a black, round, shiny ruler, heavy as dread, to knuckle us with. It hurt like fire: I remember it still. She called me Long Tongue, and I got to know only too well the wincing weight of that wielded weapon.

My other sin I was cack-handed. I'd write, tongue out and clenched between my teeth with effort, Miss Hicks forgotten, when *crack*, down came the executioner. My yell was as much because I'd bitten my tongue, as it was for the bonfire alight in my knuckles . . .

I owe Miss Hicks a debt, come to think of it: I'm still ambidextrous to this day, a great advantage, I've found.

Miss Pearce, short, plump, wore white, long-sleeved, billowy blouses, silk stockings and high-heeled shoes that, as she walked, clicked as busily as Mother's knitting needles.

Miss Pearce put me in the desk at the front. This, she said, would bridle my tongue; she'd heard what a tongue I had.

I would no more think of gabbing, offending her, than jump from the end of Smeaton's Pier into the freezing winter sea.

I loved sitting in front, nobody between Miss Pearce and me. Last lesson, she sat on my desk to read the class a story. I waited for her to take from her sleeve her little handkerchief to dab her nose before she began.

The scent from it enveloped me. I'd move an inch closer until my shoulder brushed her calf, and sit entranced, breathing that

heavenly smell – there was never scent in our house – the sweet
sound of her voice in my ears . . .

I never smell eau de Cologne now without thinking of Miss
Pearce and how she stole my heart away.

Zubes

ZUBES was the nickname we knew him by, for he was always
sucking cough sweets of that name to alleviate his perpetually
hoarse voice.

Small, wiry, wizened, he was then in his late sixties. One side
of his face was always twitching, we didn't know why. One new
boy thought he was winking at him and winked back. Oh, what
a *prabling* Mr Lawry gave him, beat him until he yelled for mercy.
And when he got home, his father, a St Ives man who'd just come
back from the States, added to the dose.

Small as he was, no boy, however big, dared to defy him. Only
one ever did to my knowledge. The disgrace he brought to his
family was such they were puzzled to devise the remedy for his
sin. Finally, they despatched their hulking, protesting son, much
to his disgust, to Mr Lawry's house, clutching his ill-spelt, ill-
written apology.

Zubes was a noted local preacher. He had taught our fathers,
caned them, too, as he caned us. Yet they – and we! – thought
the world of him.

His authority was absolute. A sagacious man, he helped our
fathers in their need, was always at their beck and call. He read
and wrote for them, pleaded their case to those above them,
whoever they were.

He had been Mayor of St Ives three times. Little wonder, then,
wherever he was seen, his old pupils greeted him, all keen to
have a word, still to call him 'sir'.

A righteous man, entirely without malice, like so many of his
fishermen friends. His secret? He knew what was right for us
boys, was quite sure he was teaching us how to live.

The one and only key: the Bible. How I wish today I still believed it were true.

Old Jan

OLD Jan was short and pot-bellied. A few straggly hairs from above his right ear were brushed across his domed speckled head to form a scanty cover. His blue eyes had prominent bags below them and these, together with the deeply-scored lines that ran from his nostrils down past the corners of his thin mouth, gave his face a permanently suffering look.

He had only one yellow fang-like tooth in the middle of his upper jaw, and only two others opposite in his lower jaw. He confiscated the packet of nicey of any boy he caught chewing. By the time the lesson ended and the boy asked for his packet back, there would be far fewer sweets in it, for Jan would help himself from time to time as he taught.

Jan's cane was long and frayed at the end. He bent the cane to and fro when he was mad – he was very short-tempered – and call you out, shouting "You fool, boy, you tomfool. Hold out your dirty paw!"

His skill was such, he never clouted your palm - that would really have hurt. Instead – you had to keep your hand quite still, not flinch – he only swished your fingertips. That stung a bit, but didn't really hurt.

You pretended it did and clog-danced about in your hobnail boots on the bare floorboards, making as much din as you could and yelling blue murder, winking at your mates.

Such exhibitions pleased Jan as much as the boys. He'd smile at the class. When you calmed down, he'd ask where your mother got you from; he'd never seen the like in all his born days. Given over with a packet of tea or changed in the cradle, were two of his usual answers.

His pal, Zubes, chewed tobacco, roll tobacco, as did his

cronies, the fishermen. Old Jan smoked only an occasional cigarette; he claimed smoking was bad for his weak chest, which kept him away from school for long periods during the winter. A fact that Zubes, who'd never missed a day's school in his long life, tartly commented on to us, without actually saying his colleague was skiving.

Jan claimed his ancestor was King of Ireland, was named O'Sullivan, deposed by treachery. We didn't know whether this was true or not, but were tickled to think we were being taught by the descendant of a king, no matter how remote in time.

Our best lesson was poetry. After clearing his mouth of one of our sweets – humbugs and *cludgy* were his favourites – he loved to recite some of the scores of poems he knew by heart.

He became quite a different person when he was reciting. His voice deepened; the rasp disappeared; the sound rounded and filled with emotion. I'd shut my eyes and listen with all my might. I can still hear him now intoning these lines from Wordsworth, his best-loved poet:

> Hence in a season of calm weather
> Though inland far we be,
> Our souls have sight of that immortal sea
> Which brought us hither,
> Can in a moment travel thither
> And see the children sport upon the shore,
> And hear the mighty waters rolling evermore.

When he finished, I opened my eyes in time to see him wiping his.

Today I know only too well why those lines brought tears, and lament that I can no longer share Wordsworth's intimations of immortality.

THE OVERCOAT COMPLAINT

"PETER!"

"'Ullaw, Silas?"

"Peter, in the name O' God cast yer eyes upon'n over there, will 'ee? Ben'dic, I mean."

"Where's he to, en?"

"Over there settin' on Dobles Wall. What in the name of Satan ez 'ee lookin' like, eh?"

"Brehmee tidy, b'lieve."

"Tidy! Dressed up like a buck rat in a bran' noo overcoat, that's 'ow tidy 'ee ez."

Peter, always one for a bit of a spree, determined to whet Silas up and said in an innocent tone "Well, Silas, 'ow shudn't one o' we from Downlong dress up in a overcoat as well as one of they gentry from Uplong?"

"'Ow shudn't we? You d'knaw as well as me 'ow we shudn't. Becuz nobody Downlong wud be seen dead in a overcoat, unless 'e's a rale invalid. Only gentry and rale invalids do wear overcoats in St Ives."

Peter scratched behind his ear with the stem of his pipe as if pondering this, then said "But Ben'dic *ez* a rale invalid."

"Rale invalid, ez 'ee!" Silas said witheringly. "I just bin waitin' for'n to 'ave the face to put on a overcoat. 'Ow he don't be struck down dead with shame, I don't knaw."

"Et's a breh 'andsome overcoat, though, Silas, edn't eh?"

"Brehmee 'andsome, sure 'nuff, Peter. But the tragedy of et ez that Ben'dic 'aven't earned et. 'E 'aven't earned bran for ducks for dunkey's years, and ere 'ee ez lashed up like Lord Muck 'isself in a noo overcoat."

"Lucky old chap."

Silas snorted in disgust. "Lucky 'e's got 'is poor old slavey of a wife to keep'n, you mean. Sluggin' away night and day for'n, as everybody d'knaw."

"Poor dear Sarah." Peter's tone showed that he truly sympathised with Benedict's wife. "A better woman never cut mawsel from a loaf."

This was enough for Silas. "You're right, Peter. What she wanted to marry that lazy laplouse for, I shall never make out. She cud 'ave 'ad plenty of others, all worth a gurryful of the likes of Ben'dic."

Silas glared ferociously in Benedict's direction, asked again "What in hell's mouth ez 'ee lookin' like?"

Peter shaded his eyes — how bright the sun was. He peered across from the Lodge to where Benedict was sitting humped up as shapeless as a net crammed with herring. He well remembered what a scandal it had been — it was all over Downlong quick as a gull could shit — when Sarah had given Silas the boot, even though they had been pledged, and married Benedict. Silas had loathed Benedict from then on: and they first cousins, in the bargain.

"You asked me what poor old Ben'dic' look like, Silas." He loaded his voice with apparent concern. "Rale poorly, I think."

Silas Perkin snorted like a seal coming up for air. "Rale poorly! I wager my life he edn't more poorly than we are."

"But," protested Peter solemnly, "I was only talkin' to 'im yesterdeh. Tellin' me all about 'is complaint, 'e was."

"Complaint!" Silas rasped out. "The only complaint 'e's got ez the overcoat complaint."

Peter winked at Fred Ninnis, standing next to them enjoying the fun, said "That edn't a very charitable thing to say about yer own first cousin, ez et?"

Fred poked his oar in, adding "You d'deny et, Silas, but 'ee *ez* yer first cousin. Yer feyther and 'is feyther was — "

"I don't care a dogfish egg about that. I don't own 'im. Never 'ave these last twenty-four years, and never shall. He's got the lurgums, that's what 'e's got, the lurgums! Work and 'e 'ave parted company for good. 'Is old feyther was a old crope, too neary to give 'ee a smile. Put on 'is overcoat when 'ee was forty-five years of age, and never done another hand's chur."

"And Ben'dic' 'isself is the same age as me," Fred said, eager to keep the game going, "so that do mean 'ee beat 'is own feyther by two year. We went to the National School together, down by the Parish Church, but that's gone now, closed down, like so many other good things."

Across the Wharf on Doble's Wall, oblivious of their presence, Benedict let the sun fall full on his face; the warmth went right through him to the very bones, it did, and eased him. How peaceable he felt – ageless, somehow, like when he was a lad . . . like when . . .

A cheerful voice interrupted Benedict's daydream. "'Ullaw, Ben, my son, 'ow's the complaint comin' on?"

"'Ullaw, Dick. Not too good at all. I've reached such a pitch now I've got to spake asy for me old throat. If I d'even raise me voice a bit, my old throat do sting so, and my old chest do ache so, I dont knaw whether I'm comin' or goin'. Sometimes I don't knaw whether it's Chres'mas or Easter."

"Well, Ben'dic', I bin sad to see 'ow fast you're goin' down 'ill. I'll wager a fleet of nets to a crabpot you wean't ever do another stroke, especially now you've took to yer overcoat." Dick could no longer keep the note of sarcasm out of his voice. "Like feyther, like son, b'lieve. So long."

Benedict jerked wide awake. "So long, Dick," he said weakly.

The tail of Dick's remark sank into him sharp as the spur of a dogfish. Why was everybody being so nasty? This was the first time Dick, a true friend, or so he thought until now, had had a go at him, but he could hardly walk by either of the two lodges these days without somebody hailing him and codding him.

And now that he'd finally put on his overcoat, he shuddered to think what some of them were going to say. That was going to be more than mortal man could stand. What a coddle he had got himself into – and all because he didn't like work.

"Ben'dic'!"

The shout was loud enough to be heard all over Downlong nearly, although it only came from the Shamrock Lodge.

Benedict recognised his cousin Silas's voice instantly. Who in this world could mistake the great harsh voice of a man who weighed nearly twenty stone in his stockinged feet? Benedict winced, closed his eyes, sank his head on his chest, pretending he hand't heard.

"Ben'dic'! You got'n on, I see."

This time the shout was even louder; what lungs that swordfish of a man had!

Everyone was by now listening: a bit of a *crant* like this was too good to be missed, better than a play. Even the women over by Laity's shop on the Wharf at the bottom of Dick's Hill, the shop stacked full of teas straight from China, where old Laity himself had once worked – all those great Ali Baba jars as high as your head and decorated with all those lovely designs, a sight for sore eyes they were – had stopped gabbing and were now all ears.

Benedict's heart was nibbling at his chest like a whiting nibbling at a baited hook. What a place to be in: what was he to do? He could have wept for very shame.

"Ben'dic'! Take they gee bundles of cotton wool out of yer lug'oles, then you'll 'ear as well as I can. . . . I see you've put'n on at last, en."

Benedict stood up, squeezed himself together as best he could. He dared not look across to where his tormentor and his gaping friends were standing. His face reddened, there was a roaring in his ears; he found it difficult to breathe. If he did not make a move now, it would be too late.

Mustering what little strength left to him, he turned and made for home.

As he fled, Simon's voice resounded in his ears like the crack of doom: "Like feyther, like son. Ben'dic' 'as got the same complaint, m'sons, as 'is feyther 'ad before 'im – the *overcoat* complaint!"

Once out of their sight, Benedict slowed down, tried to catch his breath. From Fore Street he turned sharp right into The Digey, then left into Virgin Street, where he lived.

His plan was already laid: he knew exactly what he had to do.

He pushed open the epps-door and went into the kitchen.

"'Oly 'eaven," Sarah cried, "What's the matter, Feyther? Seen a ghost, 'ave 'ee, or what? The'rt whiter'n candle grease. 'Ave 'ee 'ad a clam?"

"'Es, Sarah, I come over all queer on Doble's Wall just now. Almost fainted right away, I ded. . . . Git the doctor."

Sarah stared in despair and distress at her husband, lifting her wings of shoulders and lowering her herring-gull nose. Without even pausing to take off her pinny and throw her shawl about her shoulders, she rushed out.

At once Benedict went into the closet, seized the piece of carbolic soap lying by the washbowl, cut it into small pieces, swallowed the lot.

Dr Matthew arrived to find him in bed, vomiting violently into the flowered chamberpot.

Sarah held his forehead till be could vomit no more. Benedict flopped back on the pillow, limp as a stale ling and white as the feathers on a gannet's breast.

Dr Matthew put the thermometer in his mouth and took his pulse. Never had he felt a pulse that jerked and fluttered so. He took the thermometer out of the patient's mouth: instead of a high temperature, Benedict's was only a little above normal.

Completely mystified, the doctor turned questioningly to Sarah.

"'E's 'ad a clam, Doctor," she said. "Next, it'll be a stroke, then 'e'll be put under the turf . . . Clams do run in the family, as you d'well knaw, Doctor."

"A clam, sure 'nuff, Doctor," Benedict breathed quaveringly. "I thought I was goin' to pass away, and that's the God's truth."

Sarah said hastily "And lately 'e's bin tellin' me 'e's goin' to work agen, Doctor. 'Ave you ever 'eard tell of such a thing? 'E's in a decline, for sure. Saw the grave gapin' in front of 'n, he ded. And 'e's bin talkin' about workin'!"

"Out of the question," Dr Matthew said decisively.

"Do 'ee 'ear that, Feyther? —

"Not another blessed 'and's chur will 'ee do while I'm alive to tend to 'ee. Et edn't as if I cean't maintain 'ee."

Benedict closed his eyes to hid the gleam of triumph in them. What a treasure Sarah was. "But what are people goin' to say, Sarah? Me not workin' no more, and me of an age to be in me prime if et wadn' for the old family complaint."

Sarah cried "Lave that to Doctor Matthew 'ere." She turned to where the doctor, still bemused, was pondering how to extract himself from what the locals called this coddle. "Ben'dic' ez too thin-skinned to live, Doctor. Always worryin' about what people are goin' to say. Backbitin'! They're all backbiters. Well, let them backbite. That never broke nobody's back yet, ded et? But you'll give Ben'dic' a stercificate wean't 'ee Doctor? Plain enough fer them all to read. I - "

"Of course, Mrs Tregenza, that's the least I can do," the doctor said hastily. "We must relieve Mr Tregenza of any anxiety on that score."

Tears of grateful relief trickled down Benedict's face, by now resuming his usual healthy look. It had been ghastly swallowing that carbolic soap; it would be days before he felt like allowing any mawsel of food to pass his lips. It had been worth it, though. And soon he would get his good appetite back: Sarah would be sure to fit something really nice for him when he gave the word.

And best of all, a doctor's stercificate! Wrote plain enough for all the Doubting Thomas's to see. Wait till he waved that in his cousin Simon Perkin's face. Let him have a eyeful of that, then let's see what he would say.

Benedict lay back, luxuriating in the warmth of the bed – you can't beat a good feathered tick for mattress and pillow, even though you nearly always got a flea or two in them.

Benedict sank lower in his bed, sighed long and quietly, letting his mind dwell on what his cousin was going to look like when he read the stercificate.

"'Ow," Benedict asked himself aloud, "could I 'ave 'ad the last laugh over 'im if et 'adn't bin fer me idea of swallowin' that gee piece of carbolic?"

POLLY GARRICK

POLLY Garrick – that was the nickname Paul Stevens was known by Downlong, though nobody could remember who had so named him, and why – was already over six foot tall before he was thirteen. As he went through his teens, he broadened in proportion until the fishermen swore there wasn't a finer man to be found in the whole of St Ives.

They expected him to play for the Chiefs. Six foot three and over seventeen stone in his stockinged feet; what a second row forward he would make. . . .But no, Polly never took to rugby, nor to any other game, for that matter.

This was undoubtedly because this handsome man with hair the colour of a crab's back, eyes bright and fond as a young seal's, and a jaw with a challenging jut to it, had one ludicrous flaw in his character: despite his great size and strength, he was literally afraid of his own shadow. "That's Polly weighed up for you," they said, smiling, for everyone had a soft spot for him, "timid as a sprat chased by a mackerel."

I don't suppose you've been out in St Ives Bay of a blue May evening and seen a shoal of sprats with the mackerel after them. Their sun-fired silver spatters the surface, thrashing it into a maelstrom of fright. Well, Polly was like a sprat chased by some monster mackerel – the mackerel of his own uncontrollable imagination.

That sea is never silent. Even on the calmest summer night as he lay awake in bed, he could still hear it stirring and sighing. He'd lie there and listen . . .

Sometimes he fancied it was whispering to him, and he was comforted; sometimes he was convinced his own breathing was part of the vast breathing of the sea itself, that in some obscure way they shared the same life, and he was a little less lonely.

Full tide and full moon were magic to him. After a hunk of his mother's saffron cake and a mug of cocoa for supper, he'd tell the time aloud from their enormous grandfather clock, kiss his mother (he never forgot), and clump upstairs. He'd throw up the bottom sash of his window and sit, leaning his pugnacious chin on the sill, carefully avoiding the little pot with the even littler geranium that always seemed to be in flower and whose smell reminded him of something in his granny's house in one of her cupboards, something he couldn't put a name to.

It was a white world he looked out on, a pure thin world. The horseshoe harbour was a lake of light. Now and again an offshore breeze crinkled the water, split the light into billions of bright petals, set these evanescent petals flickering.

The delicate masts of the boats beckoned: the intimate colloquy of the boats with the water transported him.

He'd lift his eyes and follow the glittering moon track out through the harbour mouth and across the bay to the far eastern shore. Freed momentarily from the heavy burden of himself, he journeyed out and away over that track, drawn as powerfully as the high full moon draws the tides to herself.

As some sort of cover for his timidity, Polly cultivated a forceful, rasping way of speaking. If you didn't know him, you'd have thought him the most terrible man alive to get on the wrong side of. Unfortunately, before he was thirty he had pyorrhoea of the gums, a common complaint Downlong. He didn't go to Tregarthen's on the Malakoff like everybody else – you couldn't beat Tregarthen as a dentist, that was everybody's opinion – he went to a foreigner, a fly-by-night quack. The fly-by-night summarily pulled out all his teeth and found him a set of dentures several sizes too big for him. The quack then left the town in a hurry, owing all the tradesmen, especially Bennett the jeweller in Tregenna Hill. From then on, when Polly spoke, his new teeth clattered in his head like castanets. To keep them in his mouth he was forced to clench his jaws together and grind out his words ever more grimly.

Polly earned a new nickname when his relations came over from

Mousehole to spend the day. It was his neighbour, Bertha Rogers, who heard him and promptly spread it all over Downlong. She swore she heard him roar: "Mawther, I've found the breadknife. Now give me the mawsel and I'll cut the loaf. Hand me the cocoa and I'll make tay for all 'ands."

True or false, everybody Downlong dragged this saying out on every conceivable occasion, and from then on, Polly was Polly Breadknife. Some concluded he'd gone a bit soft in the head. I felt certain he put the cart before the horse deliberately, that he was in reality a natural wit, that he deliberately turned himself into a figure of fun as the only way of living with his timidity.

The incident which earned him his next nickname happened one hot summer's night. Bertha Rogers heard every last detail through the thin partition wall that separated her bedroom from his, and the story lasted her the rest of her life.

It was about half after one in the morning. The peaceful silence was broken by a tremendous thump down in the kitchen. This woke Bertha and startled her as much as it must have done her neighbours.

After a long pause Polly's mother called "Polly, my boy, wakin' are 'ee?"

"'Es, Ma."

"Ded 'ee 'ear that great thump? That's somebody down in our kitchen. Goest on down and see who et ez."

Silence, unbroken silence.

"Polly, are 'ee 'arken to me?"

"'Es, Ma."

"Ded 'ee 'ear that blackguard downstairs?"

"'Es, Ma."

Polly's teeth were now rattling in his head like the wheels of Ben Phillips's cart over the Slipway cobblestones when he was pulling a load of fish up from one of the boats.

"Well, goest on down, my son, and 'ale 'im out of our kitchen by the ears."

Silence, utter silence once more.

"Polly?"

"'Es, Ma?"

"Do 'ee want'n to come up 'ere and cut yer poor old mawther's throat in 'er bed?"

"No, Ma."

"Then go on down to once and bate the livin' daylights out ob 'n."

"'Es, Ma."

Suddenly an equally loud thump came from Polly's bedroom; he'd reached over the side of the bed, picked up his hobnailed boots and larrupped them down with all his not inconsiderable force. In his grimmest voice he shouted "Ulloh, down there."

No answer.

"I'm a man like a giant, mind, and I'm puttin' me boots up to come down to 'ee."

The silence grew longer and longer. Encouraged, Polly dragged on his boots, hitched up his longjohns, trod heavily to the top of the stairs.

"I'm comin' down this instant, mind," he shouted. "I'm a giant, seventeen stone in me stockened feet if I'm a pound, and I'm comin' down to 'ee this very instant."

There was another, but even louder, thump from the kitchen. A single leap took Polly into his mother's bedroom: an instant more and he had bolted the door behind him. . . . And he would not, and did not, move until daylight. Even then, his poor old mother had to go downstairs first.

They found the thumps had been caused by the pendulum weights in the grandfather clock falling down, a sound that echoed in the stillness of the night, enough, as Polly's mother said, to give a maid heart failure.

Bertha Rogers was the first to hear what the cause of the mysterious thumps was, so she had the complete story to put about.

From that day on, Polly's nickname was Polly Giant, a name that stuck to him for the rest of his life.

Polly's cowardice, if that was the right word for it, was in part caused by superstition. He'd believed all the time that there was no man down in the kitchen, but some Cornish sprite or other. If this were so, it was his charm stick that had let him down, a very worrying thought.

So far as I was able to discover, this charm stick was the only one left in use all over Downlong. Hung above Polly's mantlepiece, it was made of fine green Bristol glass that glowed as if it were lit from within. Five feet long, it had a curved handle like an ordinary walking stick. The magical thing was that the stick itself was not smooth, but grooved with a special thread like some gigantic screw.

At night the sprites came down the chimney, were attracted by the rich sea-green shine of the glass and settled on it. Fascinated by the spiralling thread and grooves, they began to count the number of complete turns. Of course they quarrelled: some tried to count the turns the thread made, some the turns the groove made. No one could agree on either. So engrossed were they in their quarrel, they did not notice that it was morning.

Polly would come down and light the slab fire. When it was going well, he'd gently take the stick by its handle, lift it from its brass hooks. The silk duster was always kept handy. He'd hold the end of the stick directly over the fire. With the duster he'd quickly run down the length of the stick, tumbling the sprites into the fire, where they were consumed.

Polly was also famous as a walker. One of his favourite rounds was along the cliff path past Carbis Bay, through Nut Grove, across Lelant Ferry and over Hayle Towans to Godrevy Point and back. He'd stand for a bit and admire across the narrow straights the white finger of Godrevy Lighthouse on its humped rock. . . . But it was the birds and wildflowers he'd really come for – and to drink in the quiet beauty of the cliffs and coves.

Calm weather in May month was best. The headlands to the east of Godrevy were an exultation of larks. Gulls and crows mingled in the clear air, the sun gloss on the crows brighter even than the white breasts of the gulls. When they dipped below the cliff edge they drew him to the very verge – and there he'd stand spellbound.

Above high-water mark the quiet boulders were the colour of a gull's back; in the shallows they suffered a magical sea change. Engulfed in the transparent water, they were aquamarine, fat and contented as a colony of seals. . . . And there out deeper, the oil-coloured cormorants strained over the surface in their leaden flight.

There was also the progress of the breeding colony of cormorants to note. They pitched their packed-earth nests on the very razor-edged spine of the stack that rose offshore, daring the sudden spring gales, completely inaccessible, awe-inspiring to behold.

And the flowers . . . he walked in a world of flowers. Dominating were the sheets of rosy sea pinks, not yet blanched by the spray to almost its own colour. On the slopes of some headlands the armies of yellow kidney vetch had ousted them; over large areas the two mingled, disputing the territory. The crouched blossom of the gorse was only beginning to stretch and open. And all around him as he stood was wealth: bi-coloured bird's-foot lotus, crouching violet, creeping jenny, white bladder campion, scylla and harebell delicate as fine china, yellow melilot, starred stonecrop, the orchises, hop trefoil and, in places where he did not dare to venture, the pure peaceful clusters of moon daisies.

May month in St Ives Bay is also the time when you begin whiffing for mackerel. Of an evening, Polly sat on the slip and sold his catch. It was here that the newly-appointed Sanitary Inspector, a foreigner from God only knows where, found him.

"I see you're handling those mackerel by hand," he said.

"'Es, you," Polly gritted out, "I got me boots up, so I cean't 'andle them with me feet."

"And what do you do for water?"

"Wehter? What do 'ee mane, wehter?"

"To wash in, I mean. You can't handle food unless you wash your hands first."

"Aw, wehter! Well, I got a gee bay full of say wehter out there. I do use that."

By now Polly's teeth were clacking like the tail of a lobster in a wire pot.

Those locals out and about had gathered around as soon as they saw the Inspector accost Polly: they knew Polly would cod him, have him on, make a proper tomfool of him.

The Inspector controlled himself with difficulty. "Well, I suppose you could use sea water in a pail, but what about soap? I don't see – "

"Soap?" Polly clacked, "soap? I've never used soap in all me born dehs; I got a 'arbour full of sand 'ere, look. I do use that. Better than all the soap that's ever been created."

He glared first at the Inspector, then at the crowd gathered around them. By now he was thoroughly enjoying himself: so were the spectators; they dearly loved to see a stranger bested; nuts and figs to them it was.

The Inspector muttered "Well, I shall have to report this," and walked hastily to his car.

He noticed that Polly was hard on his heels. He turned to the towering menacing figure, said hastily and placatingly, "See me back, my good man, will you. It's a bit awkward here, and I don't want to damage my new car."

"'Es, I don't exactly mind if I do," Polly said mildly.

He judged his moment to a nicety. When the back of the car was only a foot or two from the granite of Doble's Wall, he suddenly bent forward and roared "Hard-a-port now, and give 'er plenty of sheet!"

The Inspector, startled out of his wits, came down hard on the accelerator and promptly rammed the granite. He didn't get out to inspect the damage but swung his wheel into a full lock and accelerated viciously back, past the Rose Lodge and away over the Promenade.

Polly and some of his friends waved him a satisfied goodbye: it would be a long time before he came Downlong to poke his snitch into their business again.

Polly drew himself up to his full height, said "Lucky 'ee edn't a skipper, he'd lose 'is boat first time out of port." He shaded his eyes and looked across the harbour to the bright gilt town clock high up on the granite tower of the Parish Church.

"Very good of the Mayor, I'm sure," he said. "'E's given us all a noo wristwatch that always keep the right time. . . . Well, 'alf a dozen or so mack'rel left, I see. They'll make a nice bit of supper for Ma and me."

FOR EVER

TONIGHT my dream again brings me
the flying map of Cornwall.
How small on the sea,
how huge above my head
its long-legged shadow.

The long-legged shadow
fills itself with fish.
I, the boy on the boat,
enough fish aboard for supper,
row back through the shadow,
back to harbour, carrying my flasket
of shining fish in triumph home.

My tiny granite house on the Wharf,
sash windows raised waiting for me,
is no longer there,
yet stands there for ever.
The epps door that no longer exists
opens wide to welcome me in.

GLOSSARY

ballyragging	telling off
breh	very
brehmee	very
chacks	cheeks
cheeld	child
chur	little job; any bit of work
cludgy	chewy toffee
clam	fainting fit
clunk	swallow quickly and greedily
coddle	mess; mix-up
crant	joke
crope	mean person; lacking normal feelings
dab	throw
dumbledory	bumble bee
fadge	greedy person; always eating
fitten	cooked
fitty	tidy; proper
fooch	flat, heavy, sweetish lardy cake
frail	soft-sided carrier bag
fumigate	smell; stink
grampus	grey dolphin
gee	great; big
give her reach	go faster
hale	pull; haul
jailing	hurrying
kaybe	steal
linney	outhouse
lurgums	unwilling to work; pretending to be too ill to work
maygame	fun; playful teasing
morgay	dogfish

munged	kneaded
neary	mean; miserly
nicey	sweets
own	acknowledge
peasy; peasy-brained	foolish; daft
prahling	beating; whipping
shift	nightdress
slaws	very lazy
scat	knock
tap	sole of boot
slugging	working
trinklements	knick-knacks